THE UNFORGIVING HEART

When wealthy businessman Luke Rivers asks Alex Harvey to utilise her specialist skills and decorate parts of his newly purchased home, she is determined to refuse. For this is the man who was responsible for practically destroying her family, something she can never forgive — or forget. Events, however, conspire against her in the shape of her demanding and increasingly rebellious younger brother Ricky and, despite her every instinct warning against it, she finds herself doing exactly what Luke Rivers wants . . .

Books by Susan Udy
in the Linford Romance Library:

SUSAN UDY

THE UNFORGIVING HEART

Complete and Unabridged

LINFORD
Leicester

First published in Great Britain in 2008

First Linford Edition
published 2014

A catalogue record for this book is available
from the British Library.

ISBN 978–1–4448–2228–1

Published by
F. A. Thorpe (Publishing)
Anstey, Leicestershire

Set by Words & Graphics Ltd.
Anstey, Leicestershire
Printed and bound in Great Britain by
T. J. International Ltd., Padstow, Cornwall

This book is printed on acid-free paper

1

Calm down, just calm down, Alexandra Harvey firmly cautioned herself, trying very hard to ignore the shaking of her hand as she lifted the paint brush once more. It might not be him. Oh, for goodness sake! Who was she kidding? Of course it was him. Was it likely that there'd be another Luke Rivers working and living in this area?

Okay then. Think logically; rationally. No one was going to force her to phone him back. She was her own boss, and nothing, absolutely nothing, would persuade her to do anything for that man, let alone decorate his house. Not after what he'd done.

She screwed up the piece of kitchen roll upon which she'd scribbled his phone number and threw it, to join all the other bits of rubbish which had accumulated around her. There —

problem solved. She just hoped she'd be able to drive him from her mind with as much ease.

The woman who'd rung her had sounded cool and utterly confident: 'I want a quotation for the redecoration of two rooms.' There'd been no 'good morning', no preliminaries of any kind. *I mean*, Alex now reflected, *common politeness would surely have demanded she make some sort of effort.* But no. The woman had continued: 'When can you do it?'

Alex had felt a stab of irritation. 'I'm right in the middle of something and I don't have my diary to hand. I'll have to ring you back after six o'clock.'

'Certainly. In that case, the number you will need is . . . ' The woman had given a mobile phone number. 'The interested party is Luke Rivers. I'm his PA. It's him you'll be speaking to.'

And that had been that. The woman had hung up, leaving Alex to let out a long, slow hiss of dismay.

★　★　★

It was much later that afternoon before Alex climbed into her van, glancing with pride, as she invariably did, at the foot-high letters inscribed on the side. Something Special was really starting to take off. Word was getting around that she could perfect almost any paint effect that was required. She could make an ordinary fireplace look like marble, or a plain wall resemble ancient stonework. The college course she'd taken had seen to that. That, and then a bank loan just six months ago, had been what had got her started. Before then, she'd spent her days in a solicitor's office, typing out lengthy legal documents and answering the phone. Then someone — she couldn't recall who now — had mentioned how difficult it was to get anything a bit special done in the decorating trade, and — hey presto! Here she was, with a flourishing business and enough work to keep her busy for the next two months.

Alex glanced at her watch, yawning and stretching her aching back as she did so. Too late to start something else now; although she did, when circumstances demanded, often work until much later. Not tonight, though. She was tired. She'd pay a flying visit to her closest friend, Annie, who should be home by now. They didn't see nearly enough of each other anymore, what with the demands of Alex's business and the varying hours that Annie worked. Annie was a nurse and, when Alex had rung her just two evenings ago, her friend had said she was working days this week. Although, Alex sighed, her younger brother, Ricky, would have been back from school for over an hour by now and would, no doubt, be wanting his tea. He was always starving by the end of the day. Maybe she ought to go straight home? Reluctantly deciding to forego her visit to her friend, she was just about to turn the ignition key when her mobile phone rang.

'Something Special. Alex Harvey speaking.'

An abrupt voice cut her words off. 'Luke Rivers. I thought you were going to ring me.'

Alex smothered a gasp. She'd forgotten all about him and, just a few hours ago, she would have deemed that impossible. 'I'm sorry.' She glanced at her watch again. 'Although it isn't quite six yet. And I did say it would be after that.'

'It doesn't bode well for your business if you don't return your calls.'

'I was about to — '

For the second time, it was as if she hadn't spoken. 'As I understand it,' he was saying, 'you're a relatively new enterprise. Ignoring a potential customer is an ... unusual method of running a business. I'll have to try it, see if it works for me.' His tone now was one of pure sarcasm. Smoothly spoken but, nonetheless, sarcasm.

Alex felt her temper begin to rise. She wasn't a redhead for nothing. Her green eyes flashed and her lips, usually full and soft, tightened and hardened. An angry flush mounted her creamy, lightly freckled face as the fingers of her free hand tightened upon the rim of the steering wheel.

'You're quite right, *Mister* Rivers.' She deliberately emphasised the title — she wanted him to know that she had manners, even if his had deserted him. He was as bad as his PA. 'I am a new business, which means I can't afford to ruin hours of work. When you're working with the medium that I have been using all day, you have to keep going. I would have rung you in a few moments.' She surprised herself. She wasn't usually such a glib liar. She'd had no intention of phoning him back.

'Really!' was his curt response to her excuse. 'Well, I've beaten you to it. When can you come to the house and have a look?'

Determined to start as she meant to go on, she said, 'I'm rather busy at the present time — '

'You can come and have a look, surely? Give me a price?'

'We-ell, I suppose I could.'

'Okay. So, when?' Good grief, the man was like a steamroller. What was she going to do?

Out of the blue, a brilliant idea came to her. She'd go first thing tomorrow morning, then quote him a price so ridiculously high that he'd be bound to turn her down. Because wild horses wouldn't make her work for this man.

'Shall we say eight o'clock tomorrow morning? Or is that too early?' she provocatively asked.

'That will suit me fine.'

'Right. If you'd like to give me your address?'

'Certainly. It's Grayling Manor. I've just bought it.'

'Why, that's in Kingston Prior!' And uncomfortably close to her and her brother, Ricky.

'It most certainly is. How clever of you.'

Alex tightened her lips once again. More sarcasm. Even if she hadn't already hated and despised him, she most certainly would now. It just reinforced her decision not to have anything to do with him. Alex's heart clenched at the memory of what had happened eight years ago. And it was all this man's fault.

'Not really. I've lived here all my life. I know every house in the town.'

'Good. You'll know the state that most of the manor's in then.'

'Well,' she said, hating to admit to it, 'I haven't actually been inside.'

'Have you not?' He sounded as if he were grinning. He'd guessed she wouldn't have been inside. He would know only too well that someone like her wouldn't mix in the same social circles as the previous owners.

'Well, now's your chance, Miss Harvey. I presume it is 'Miss' and not 'Missus'?'

'It is.' Alex ground the words out from between clenched teeth. He'd somehow managed to make her single state sound like a failing on her part. Why? Because he was married himself by this time and so despised anyone who wasn't? After all, he must be in his thirties now, so it was reasonable to suppose he had a wife. He'd been twenty-something at the time of it all; she'd never known his exact age. But, if he was married, how come it was him calling her and not his wife?

'Okay, that's settled then,' he went on. 'Eight o'clock it is. I'll look forward to it.'

Which is more than I will, Alex grimly decided as she switched her phone off. She would definitely go and see Annie. Ricky would have to wait for his tea. She needed to talk to someone, right now.

2

Annie's response was totally predictable. 'You're kidding!' she gasped. 'Luke Rivers phoned you? Why?'

'He wants some decorating done,' Alex told her. 'He's bought Grayling Manor.'

'Has he? I'd heard it was sold but no one seemed to know who to. So,' Annie continued, eyeing her speculatively, 'are you going to do it?'

'No way! I've had to agree to quote, but as for taking the job . . .'

'Go on — what?' Annie urged.

'I'll quote him a huge amount and hope he turns it down.'

Annie frowned. 'I don't understand. If you really don't want to do it, why not just say no — that you're too busy or something?'

'I tried that. The man's like a steamroller. Before I knew it, I was agreeing to go to the house.'

'My goodness! Whatever is Ricky going to say — and Lauren?'

'They won't know anything about it. As I said, I've no intention of taking on the job. He'll say no when he hears the price that I've got in mind.'

Annie looked doubtful. 'I hope you're right. The way I've heard it, he's worth a small fortune with a finger in practically every pie known to man.'

'You didn't tell me you'd heard anything about him since — '

'No, well, I know how hearing his name upsets you. Look, Alex, can you afford to turn down a job — any job? I mean, there is the bank loan to pay back, and then there's the upkeep on that tin can that you so optimistically call a van, plus your living expenses — and they don't come cheap these days.'

'I know.' Alex grinned ruefully. 'But, luckily, I'm booked up for the next few weeks.'

11

'Maybe you should forget your scruples?'

'Forget that he was the cause of my parents' deaths? Is that what you're saying?' Alex's eyes stung with tears. 'That's hardly having scruples, Annie. It's more a case of staying loyal to their memory.'

'I know, lovey, but life has to go on. They wouldn't want you to go on grieving like this. They loved you and Ricky more than anything.'

With that, Alex's thoughts reverted to that dreadful time. Normally she managed to keep the memories at bay, but listening to Annie talking about her parents and knowing that the following day she was going to have to face the man who, in her opinion, was responsible for their deaths was more than enough to resurrect all the pain and anguish.

She'd been twenty-one, Ricky seven. Lauren, their cousin who'd lived with them since the age of three, had been nineteen — just. Alex could see her now, her face radiant as she danced into the house one evening, saying she'd met this 'fab' guy.

'Luke Rivers. He's a bit older than me, but — '

'How old?' Alex's mother, Beth, had anxiously asked. She'd always regarded Lauren as her own child and treated her as such, even though Lauren's living with them had never been made official. Which meant that Lauren had kept her own surname, a circumstance that Beth had regretted. She'd thought the little girl would feel more a part of the family if she assumed the same name as the rest of them, but Lauren hadn't wanted that. It was as if by holding onto her own surname, she kept hold of her mother too.

Lauren's mother was the sister of Alex's father, and in the wake of her husband's death from cancer she had rejected the small girl in favour of a new man and a new life in Australia. To try and compensate for this, Beth had always tended to treat the girl more leniently than her own children. If Beth and John hadn't taken her in, she would most certainly have ended up in some sort of foster home, or worse. Especially as nothing had been heard of her mother since.

Alex remembered Lauren looking a bit shifty at that point. 'Um, in his twenties.'

'Oh, Lauren,' Beth had exclaimed. 'He's not too old for you, is he?'

'No, Mum.'

She'd always called Beth and her husband Mum and Dad. Hardly surprising, really. At three she'd loved to mimic five-year-old Alex, or Sandra as she'd called her, and still did. She'd been quite unable to master the full name of Alexandra. It had been only in the last five or six years that Alex herself had shortened her name. It had been her mother who had insisted everyone call her Alexandra.

'I can handle him,' Lauren had confidently declared. 'He's a pussycat.'

And she'd seemed able to, for a

while. The Harvey family never met him, because while she was dating him Lauren had got a job as a trainee hair stylist and beautician at a salon in the nearby town of Dorrington. Not long after, she found herself a house-share in the same town and left the Harvey home. Although she came back on a regular basis, she never once brought Luke with her, despite Beth and John frequently asking her to. Alex had wondered at the time how much of a hand Luke Rivers had had in Lauren's desertion of the family home. He'd lived in Dorrington also. Having Lauren close would have been very convenient — as well as removing her from beneath the watchful guardianship of her aunt and uncle.

Then one evening, some three months or so later, the phone had rung. Beth had answered it. 'Oh, Lauren, darling, I'm so sorry . . .' There'd been a silence, and then, 'No, Lauren, don't do anything silly. You promise? Right — Dad and I will be right there.' She'd slammed the phone down and turned to her husband. 'Come on, John. We have to go, now. Luke Rivers has finished with Lauren — just like that.' She snapped her fingers. 'She's devastated and threatening to kill herself.'

They'd rushed from the house, and that had been the last time that Alex had seen them alive. On the way to Lauren's, their car had collided head-on with an articulated lorry. Beth had been killed instantly, and John had died an hour later on the operating table.

Alex recalled now the pain of having to tell seven-year-old Ricky that both his parents were dead. Lauren had been no help at all; her grief had literally paralysed her.

It had all been left to Alex: to arrange the funeral and sell the family home, so that she and Ricky could move into a more manageable and smaller terraced house; and to be both father and mother to Ricky. There'd been times when she'd thought they wouldn't survive it, any of them. Lauren, not unexpectedly, as well as being grief-stricken, had also been overwhelmed with guilt.

'If they hadn't been in such a panic over me, Dad wouldn't have been driving too fast, and it wouldn't have happened!' she'd wailed and sobbed.

Alex had been lost for words because at the time she had held Lauren at least partly responsible. The larger portion of the blame, though, she'd attached firmly to Luke Rivers, for his brutally callous treatment of her cousin. However, as time had passed, her anger had eased and she'd more or less forgiven Lauren.

But Luke Rivers?

No, she'd found it impossible to forgive him. Surely, she'd told herself over and over, a man in his twenties should have realised how his harsh treatment would affect a love-struck girl of nineteen — a girl who'd lost a father to cancer at the age of two and a half and then been rejected and deserted by her mother just months later. Because surely Lauren would have told him about that? And surely he could have reasoned that yet another rejection, even one that was happening many years later, could well prove too much for her to cope with. If he had known — and she'd never questioned Lauren about that, she had to admit — he clearly hadn't cared.

But Ricky had remained her chief concern. The little boy had continually wept and pleaded for his parents to come back, and had suffered from nightmares for weeks. But for Annie, Alex sometimes thought she would have had a breakdown or worse. Her friend had been a pillar of strength: always there, always sensible, pragmatic — just like now.

'If you start turning down jobs for purely personal reasons, you won't last five minutes,' Annie now pointed out.

'It's just one job, Annie. And he was the one responsible for their deaths. You know he was.' She covered her face with her hands as the enormity of what she was going to have to confront the next day struck her.

'To be fair, Alex,' Annie said as she gently pulled Alex's hands away from her face, 'he wasn't to know that Lauren would threaten to kill herself. And they had only been seeing each other for a relatively short while. He may not have realised how . . . emotionally involved she had become.'

'But he could have let her down gently, surely? She was only nineteen, and immature with it. He must have recognised that,' Alex agonised tearfully. 'You should have heard him on the phone just now, Annie. Abrupt to the point of rudeness. And sarcastic! He could give a master class on the art.'

A man walked into the room at that point. His gaze took in the little scene before him: Alex's distress and Annie's clear anxiety, and he mouthed at Annie, 'What's up?'

Alex smiled weakly at him. 'Hi, Rob.' She dashed her tears away. 'Don't mind me. Annie, I have to go.'

'Don't run away on my account.' He strode across to Annie and kissed her. He then turned to Alex and gave her a hug. 'Anything you can tell me about?'

Alex sighed. She envied the two of them, although she was at a loss to understand why every time Rob asked her to marry him, Annie refused. It wasn't that she didn't love him; she always said she did. She just felt that they were so happy that she didn't want to rock the boat. Alex had often wondered if her friend simply wasn't ready to settle down, despite the fact that she and Rob now lived together. Annie had been known to flirt madly with other men during her and Alex's infrequent nights out together. Not that that was surprising, Alex wryly concluded; the men practically fell over each other to get to her. She'd have to be Superwoman to resist them. Not that it ever went further than flirting.

Annie was the possessor of a petite but extremely well-shaped body: a perfect thirty-four, twenty-three, thirty-four. She also possessed a heart-shaped face, large china-blue eyes, and a mouth that simply begged to be kissed. Alex would have given anything for the same.

Instead, at five-feet-seven, Alex's breasts were nicely rounded but too small in her opinion; she could have done with at least another couple of inches. She also rated her hips too slim and her legs too long. Her face, framed by bobbed red hair as it was, she deemed attractive, but nothing out of the ordinary, even taking into account her startlingly green, long-lashed eyes and full, rose-pink lips.

Yet, she reasoned, she couldn't be that bad; she'd never been short of boyfriends — when she had the time, that was, which wasn't often nowadays, what with running her own business and bringing up her younger brother single-handedly: a task that was, despite her love for him, becoming increasingly difficult. At fifteen, Ricky was rebellious and resentful more often than not and becoming increasingly hard to handle.

'You've met Luke Rivers, haven't you, Rob?' Annie was now asking.

'Well, not actually met him, but I've heard a lot about him. I was in the same room as him on one occasion.'

'What's he like?'

'Okay.' Rob shrugged. 'Typical high-powered businessman. Always on the go, dynamic, very involved in the engineering and manufacturing indus- tries. He took over several ailing factories and literally dragged them back into profit. He's also fairly recently gone into the leisure business.'

'But what does he look like?' This question again was from Annie.

'Good-looking in a buccaneer-ish sort of way, I suppose. The women certainly flock round him. Why?'

'He's asked Alex to quote on a decorating job. Did you know he'd bought Grayling Manor?'

Rob whistled through his teeth. 'No, has he?' He wrinkled his brow. 'Wow!

I'd have said you were on to a good thing there, Alex. He's got money coming out of his ears. And from what I've heard, the whole place needs doing up. You could be kept busy for months.'

'Oh, Rob,' Annie exclaimed in exasperation, 'he was the one who dumped Lauren.'

'Oh, yeah — of course. Sorry, forgot. A bit tricky that, then, given your opinion of him.'

'You could say that,' Alex riposted.

'Still, business is business, and it was all a long time ago.' He regarded Alex thoughtfully. 'He could provide you with a lot of work, Alex. His latest acquisition is a string of hotels, and I've heard that some of them need substantial refurbishing. He could be a good man to keep in with.'

'That's more or less what I've been saying to her,' Annie put in. 'She can't afford to turn work down.'

'I'll think about it,' Alex said. 'Look, I must go. Ricky will be so hungry by now, he'll have stripped the fridge of any evidence of food if past experience is anything to go by.'

'You'll think about what we've said — promise?'

'Yes, I promise.' But Alex had no intention of taking on the Luke Rivers job, even if she had to say no directly to the man himself.

3

The following morning, a little later than she'd promised, Alex parked her van alongside a metallic green, top-of-the-range Range Rover. Normally she had no trouble with it, but today of all days she'd had difficulty getting it started. Maybe it had sensed her reluctance to meet Luke Rivers and was showing solidarity?

She smiled grimly to herself as she climbed from the van to stand and stare up at Grayling Manor. It was an elegant building, constructed of rose-red brick, and built in the middle of the eighteenth century, she believed. Of course she'd seen it many times before from the road, but it looked even more impressive close up. A steeply sloping grey tiled roof topped neat rows of small-paned sash windows. An attractive fanlight sat above the front door.

Even before she rang the bell, it opened and a man stood there. 'Not a good omen,' were his first words. 'You're over five minutes late.' He must have been watching out for her.

'S-sorry,' Alex stammered, feeling immediately wrong-footed — just when she'd wanted to be in control of the situation from the start. 'My van wouldn't start.'

She saw Luke Rivers's gaze go beyond her and then watched, outraged, as a broad smile wreathed his face. 'I'm not surprised. It looks like the perfect candidate for the scrap heap,' he bluntly retorted.

Alex tightened her lips but didn't respond.

'You'd better come in.' He stood to one side in order to allow her to pass him.

Alex did so, her every sense heightened due to his proximity — but also because he was almost too handsome to be true. He must be at least six-foot-one or-two — he certainly topped her by a good six or seven inches — with hair the colour of a raven's wings, a pair of eyes that were equally dark beneath straight brows, a slightly aquiline nose, skin that could almost be described as swarthy as it was so tanned, and a devastatingly attractive cleft in a chin and jawline that she would have sworn had been hewn from a solid block of granite.

She recalled Rob's description of him: buccaneer-ish. It fitted him to a T. No wonder nineteen-year-old Lauren had fallen hook, line and sinker. Still, at a more mature twenty-nine, Alex would be safe.

He was still gazing at her van, she noticed. 'How long have you had it? I'm astonished it's still running.'

'Of course it's still running,' she waspishly assured him. 'It's very reliable, actually.'

He cocked an eyebrow at her. 'Don't you mean reliable until this morning?'

'I'm sure that was just a blip,' she assured him.

'Let's hope you're right.' The dryness of his tone suggested he didn't share her confidence.

For the first time since she'd been inside, Alex glanced around. They were standing in a large square hallway with a black-and-white tiled floor and a beamed ceiling. An uncompromisingly straight staircase led upstairs. There were various items of antique furniture placed about, as well as several large portraits on all the walls. She wondered if they were ancestors of his. They certainly looked forbidding enough.

Alex pulled a notepad and pen from her bag. Business-like and efficient, that was how she aimed to appear. Not someone full of hate and bitterness as she really was. She didn't want him to suspect that she was deliberately inflating her quotation in order to put him off.

'Right,' she said, 'if you show me the rooms you want redecorated, I can make notes and then get back to you with a quote.'

'Fine,' he murmured.

Purely out of curiosity, she asked, 'How did you hear of Something Special?'

'You were personally recommended.' His dark eyes glinted, several tiny specks of gold suddenly gleaming in the ebony depths. 'I only ever deal with people who come vouched for.'

'I see. And may I ask who vouched for me?'

'The Gibsons. You decorated a couple of rooms for them. The effect wasn't quite to my taste,' he went on, 'but I was impressed with the standard of the workmanship.'

'Thank you.' She felt an involuntary stab of pleasure at his complimentary words. Their tastes obviously coincided. She hadn't cared for the over-elaborate paint effects that the Gibsons had demanded either. They hadn't suited either the style of the house (modern) or the furnishings (minimalist).

'Okay. Now, there are two rooms I want done, primarily: the dining room and the drawing room. I am actually living here now, having purchased some furniture from the Gladwyns just to tide me over.' He eyed her quizzically. 'Did you know them?'

'No.'

'They were downsizing, so didn't have room for everything. I still have to buy a lot more, of course. I moved from something much more modest.' He smiled warmly at her, making Alex's heart miss a beat — or three — at the transformation that that simple action induced. 'The door to your right is the dining room.'

Alex walked in, followed so closely by Luke that she could feel his breath warm upon her neck. She lengthened her stride in a deliberate attempt to put more distance between them. The further away she stayed from him, the better. She looked around the room.

'The patterned paper's completely wrong in my view,' he said.

Alex mutely agreed. The room was large, well-lit by three windows, and beamed in exactly the same manner as the hall. The walls cried out for something plain; textured, maybe.

'Well,' Alex said, clearing her throat, 'I think maybe if I frottage — ' She was sure Luke Rivers would never have heard of the process, so she could quote any price she wanted and he would be none the wiser.

'What's that? Explain.'

Alex flushed at his brusquely authoritarian tone. 'Sheets of newspaper are pressed onto thinned paint to produce random patterns. The finish can be made to resemble ancient parchment.'

'Interesting.'

'I can show you an example.' Still trying to give the impression of being genuinely interested in doing the job, she pulled a couple of books from her capacious bag. She caught a flash of something that looked like amusement upon his face.

'You haven't got your brushes and paint in there as well by any chance, have you?'

The gold glints were back in his eyes. Alex stiffened. He was laughing at her. Ignoring the urge to slap him down with a few carefully chosen words, she leafed through the pages of both books until she found an illustration of the finish. She was tempted to throw the books at him. Maybe that would teach him to curb his sarcasm. However, she contented herself with merely thrusting them at him, only to have him take them, one in each hand, without as much as the fumble that she'd hoped for. The majority of people would most likely have dropped at least one, she irritably decided.

'Yes, we'll go for that,' he murmured.

They went on into the drawing room. This had the same sort of over-decorated look as the dining room. There were no beams in here, but there was a magnificent pale stone fireplace taking pride of place on one wall. An apricot glaze would look wonderful against it.

Alex stopped right there. She had no

intention of actually taking on the work. Still, she had to make him think she would.

'I think glazing,' she said. Once again she showed him an example, this time from a single book. It was a complete waste of time trying to make him look clumsy and ridiculous. He would successfully outmanoeuvre her every time, she was sure. Thank heavens she wasn't going to be working for him.

After no more than the briefest of glances, he said, 'Perfect! I'll leave you to your measuring, or whatever it is you have to do. I have some phone calls to make. How long will you be, do you think?'

'Not long. I've brought a camera with me. I'll take several photos if that's okay. It helps me to remember things.'

'Go ahead. I'm in the room across the hall. Give me a shout when you've finished.'

★   ★   ★

Just in case he should come back, Alex took a few notes and several photographs of both rooms. He might get suspicious if he caught her doing nothing. She'd work out some basic figures and then treble them. If he was as astute a businessman as Rob had seemed to believe, that should be more than enough to deter him from taking her on. He might have pots of money, but she was sure he wouldn't want to throw it around willy-nilly.

She had wondered if he'd know who she was; know her name from Lauren. Clearly he didn't. But then if Lauren had ever spoken about her, she would have called her Sandra rather than Alex. And as their surnames were also different, he'd have no earthly reason to connect the two of them. Would he?

Briskly, she walked back into the hall, clearing her throat noisily as she did so. The door on the opposite side of the hall opened and Luke Rivers appeared. 'Finished already?' He looked surprised.

Alex nodded, trying to disregard the guilt that surged within her at the thought of what she intended to do. It went against every one of her principles.

'It didn't take long.' He sounded . . . sceptical. Was he questioning her ability to make a proper judgement on what needed doing?

'It's just a case of measuring to see how much paint I need. That doesn't take long, even for someone like me.'

Luke looked taken aback at the harshness of her tone. 'No, I suppose it wouldn't. Well, I'll see you out, shall I?'

'Thank you. I'll ring you with the quotation.'

'Good. The sooner, the better. I want to get on with it now. I don't think I can live any longer with that wallpaper.' He gave an abrupt laugh. 'We'll talk starting dates when you ring.'

Alex thought that sounded as if he'd already made up his mind to accept her price. Maybe she'd better multiply the total by four just to make sure he turned it down.

'We-ell, I am booked up for the foreseeable future — '

'I'm sure we can work something out.' He gave her the sort of smile that simply oozed self-confidence.

Luke Rivers, Alex was beginning to suspect, was a force to be reckoned with. Which meant that what he wanted, he invariably got. Well, that was about to change. She walked across to her van and climbed in.

'Are you sure that thing's roadworthy?' he asked with a broad grin.

'Of course,' Alex primly replied. 'I go everywhere in it.'

'Such faith! I wouldn't trust it to the end of the drive.'

'It's never let me down.' Confidently — defiantly, even — she turned the ignition key, only to hear a long, slow groan and nothing else. She tried again, clenching her teeth together and muttering beneath her breath, 'Come on. Don't do this to me, not now, not here — ple-ease.'

After the third futile turn of the key, she knew she'd got a problem.

She climbed back out and walked to the front of the bonnet. She lifted it to stand peering down into the engine's depths, not having a clue as to what she was looking for but hoping to find it anyway, to wipe the smug grin from Luke Rivers's face if nothing else.

4

Trying to at least look as if she knew what she was doing, Alex busily tweaked a lead or two.

'I think,' a voice murmured from just behind her right shoulder, 'you'll find it's your battery. Do you do a lot of short journeys?'

'Well, yes,' she muttered with bad grace, 'I suppose I do. I've been working locally these past few weeks.'

'I think the best thing we can do is to jump-start it off mine. It will at least get you going for now. Do you have a lead?'

'A lead?' Alex looked at him in some bemusement.

'Jump lead.'

'Oh, no. I um, I don't think so.'

'Okay. I'll get mine.'

He walked away in the direction of a large building to one side of, but separate from, the house. Alex did briefly wonder why he'd have such a thing as a jump lead. She had no doubt he only drove new cars, if the Range Rover parked just feet away was anything to go by. However, after only a moment or two, he returned.

'Success.' He smiled triumphantly at her, waving the lead aloft.

Alex felt her heart once again miss several beats. That smile, when he bothered to turn it on, was nothing short of mind-blowing.

'Haven't had to use it for a while, but still, never mind. I haven't forgotten how.'

He hadn't. Within seconds, her engine was running.

'Thank you very much.' Alex was, by this time, feeling extremely foolish in the light of her protestations about her van's reliability. Nonetheless, she held out a hand to him. He took it. She couldn't help noticing that he had a nice hand — smooth, with long fingers and well-cared-for nails. She felt a grudging pang of approval. A man's hands had always been the first things she looked at. If they'd been neglected — or worse still, in her eyes, grubby — that had been that; her interest would wane and a rejection would swiftly follow. However, in this instance — and as perfect as Luke's were — she didn't allow her fingers to linger in his, and within seconds she was climbing back into her van. It didn't help her frame of mind to discover that she was trembling.

'Okay?' He leant down towards her. His expensive aftershave filled her nostrils. 'I'll be hearing from you. Straight to a garage, now, and get that battery checked.'

★   ★   ★

By the time Alex returned home that afternoon, she was exhausted. It had been an extremely long day, with most of it spent on her knees, glazing a wooden fireplace to look like marble. So, when she unlocked the front door

40

and was greeted with a blast of rock music, it wasn't altogether surprising that her temper should flare.

'Ricky,' she shouted, 'turn it down, please.'

When he ignored her, she strode to the sitting room door and thrust it open. A group of young men — all about her brother's age, she guessed, although a closer glance showed that a couple of them might be a bit older — lounged around in the armchairs or lay spread-eagled on the floor.

'Turn it down, please.' She repeated the request and when that, too, was ignored, said, 'Or better still, turn it off.'

Ricky scowled at her but did go and lower the volume. It was the signal for the other boys to struggle to their feet. As they did so, several empty lager cans rolled onto the carpet.

Alex stared at her brother. 'Have you been drinking?'

'So what if I have been?' He looked sullenly at her; it was a look she was becoming increasingly familiar with. Not for the first time, she would have exchanged all she possessed to have her parents still around. They'd have known how to deal with Ricky's rebelliousness, and his sheer wilfulness on occasion.

'You're fifteen, Ricky. Too young to be drinking.'

'Oh get real, Sis. We all drink now. Nobody thinks anything of it.'

'Well, I do.'

'Okay, Rick man, we're off.' The other youths began to file from the room. 'It's gettin' too heavy for us.'

'Yeah, bye. See you tomorrow.'

Once they were alone, Alex swung back to her brother. 'What do you think Mum and Dad would say, Ricky?'

'Oh, gimme a break. All my friends drink. It's only lager, Alex, for goodness sake.'

Alex decided to change tack. 'Have you got any homework?'

'Yeah.' The sullen look was back.

'Right. Well, pick up those cans and then go and do it while I get supper.'

Alex sighed as she headed for the kitchen. The room stank of cigarettes. She opened a window. As if she didn't have enough to contend with in running a business and a home, she also had an increasingly defiant brother on her hands.

'Uh, Alex?'

'Yes?' She swung to face her brother.

'I've got a letter from school.'

Now what? 'What have you been doing?' she wearily asked. She would never want to be rid of Ricky, but there were times when she felt she simply couldn't cope.

'Isn't that typical of you?' Ricky exploded. 'Always so quick to think the worst of me. Well, for your information, it's not about any wrongdoing of mine; it's about a school trip next winter. Skiing in Austria.'

'Oh, I see.' Alex ran a finger under the flap of the envelope and read the words printed on the piece of paper inside. 'I can't afford this.'

'I knew it!' Ricky instantly flared up.

'You always say that.'

'That's not true. You've been on several trips.'

'Huh! Day trips, yeah.'

'Look, Ricky, I'm struggling to repay a bank loan. I've only just started the business. I have to plough any profit back in after I've deducted our living expenses.'

'B-but we must have money. What about the sale of the house? You can't have spent it all. And Mum and Dad must have left something?'

'They did, but it's all gone. How do you think we've lived these past eight years? I wasn't earning much at the time. And as for the house, there was still a lot owing on it. And if you take into account the fact that the value had dropped because of the bypass being built right behind it, well, there wasn't much left after everything was settled, and then I had to put a deposit on this place.' She shrugged. 'We only have what I earn now, Ricky, and it doesn't run to expensive skiing trips. Sorry.'

'Sorry, sorry. Is that it?' Ricky's eyes glistened with tears of rage and frustration. 'All my mates are going. I'll be the only one not to.'

'I know, but I don't see how it's possible.'

★   ★   ★

That evening Alex sat with her head bent over the details for the Grayling Manor job and came up with a figure that Luke Rivers would be bound to accept. She instantly multiplied it by three. The total now ran into thousands rather than hundreds: a sure-fire guarantee that he'd turn her down. No one — not even someone as rich as Luke Rivers — would pay that much for just a two-room makeover.

She'd ring him now. Oh Lord! His number. What was it?

It was no good checking the list of received calls on her mobile phone. She'd deleted them: something she did on a daily basis, only keeping the ones she really wanted to reply to. So she hadn't intended to get rid of Luke Rivers's number — at least, not until after she'd phoned him. It had been entirely accidental. A quick flick of a button — too quick, she sometimes thought. It was all too easy to make a mistake, as she had in this instance. To make matters worse, she'd also thrown away the piece of paper that she'd jotted the number down on.

Luckily, the bag of rubbish that she'd cast it into was still outside the back door. She ran out and emptied it onto the ground. She found the scrap of kitchen roll almost immediately. She smoothed it out and there was the number she needed.

Slowly, she walked back inside and straight into the hall and the phone. She just wanted to get this over with. Even so, her hand hovered over the phone as she studied her figures once more. It was a good job even before she inflated the price. Could she afford to turn it down? Memories of Ricky's angry face came back to her. But he wouldn't want her to do it, not if he knew who it was for. Not even for the sake of a school trip. Would he?

Suddenly she was no longer sure. Her brother had changed; was still changing. Appearances had become important to him; hence his cry of, 'All my mates will be going.' Was she being fair to him, turning this down? And what was it Rob had said? 'He could provide you with a lot of work, Alex. He's just bought up a string of hotels.' What should she do? Could she really afford to allow her personal feelings to interfere with her expanding business? With being able to provide Ricky with the better things in life?

She'd let fate decide.

If Luke Rivers accepted her final price, she'd do it. She didn't have to tell Ricky who she was working for. Still, her fingers hovered over the phone. What about Lauren? Supposing she asked who Alex was working for? Her cousin would be furious. She still held a deep grudge against Luke. It hadn't diminished one iota over the years, any more than Alex's had. Maybe that was why she still hated him so profoundly — because Lauren seemed to? Still, Luke Rivers would be extremely unlikely to accept her quote; it was disproportionately high. No one in their right mind would agree. So her worries were needless.

Luke answered on the first ring.

'M-Mr Rivers,' she haltingly began.

'Aah, Miss Harvey. How nice to hear from you so promptly. How did you get on with your van?'

'Fine. I've had a new battery fitted.'

'Good, good. Can't have you stuck on your own somewhere, miles from help of any sort. Not these days.'

Alex frowned. If she didn't know what a ruthless, cold-hearted individual he was, she'd really believe that he cared about her well-being. However, she did know, so she dismissed his words as just that: words.

'I'm sure that won't happen. Now,

about this quotation.'

'Yes?'

She told him the outrageous price she'd come up with and waited for the laugh of disbelief, the exclamation of shock. To her astonishment, she heard neither.

'I see. Fine, I accept — on the understanding that you begin straight away.'

Alex was lost for words. She'd never believed — not for a second, despite her decision to accept whatever fate decided on her behalf — that he'd agree. She could only think that he must be used to paying enormously inflated prices for whatever he wanted. So, how come he'd made himself so much money? He hadn't struck her as being a man who would be easily conned. Far from it. She'd had him down as extremely shrewd.

'Miss Harvey, are you still there?'

'Oh, yes; something diverted my attention for a moment. Um, start straight away? I can't do that. I have several other clients waiting; it wouldn't be fair to them.'

'I'll add another five hundred pounds to the total if you do.'

Alex gasped; she couldn't help herself.

'I really do want *you* — ' Luke began.

Alex held the receiver away from her and stared at it, aghast. He couldn't possibly mean what that sounded like. What was he up to?

' — to do this job, Miss Harvey,' he finished. 'You've come extremely highly recommended.'

She couldn't refuse, scruples or no scruples, she reluctantly decided. It would enable her to pay off a large chunk of her bank loan. And Ricky . . . well, Ricky could go skiing.

But it was no good; she simply couldn't overcharge him to such an outrageous extent, not even if he was the detested Luke Rivers. Her sense of fair play, always fairly active, had kicked in. And it simply wouldn't permit her to do such a thing. The problem was, though, how she was going to explain the overcharge without sounding like a complete idiot. Still, she had to try.

'Okay, I'll do it. But, um, looking at the figures I've got here, I — um, do you know, I think I might have transposed a couple of them by mistake. The total seems a bit too high.'

'Surely not,' Luke replied. 'I thought how reasonable it was for such a specialised job. Let's leave it as agreed.'

'B-but — ' Alex began to protest. Guilt was practically submerging her.

'No, I insist, Miss Harvey. I'm happy to pay for expertise such as yours. So, when can you start?'

There seemed no point in arguing with him. He was clearly determined to hire her whatever the cost. It made her feel fractionally better about her extortionate quotation. And maybe he was right; maybe she did underprice herself? Others had commented upon her cheapness. Perhaps she ought to review her costing methods?

'I'll start on Monday.' She blurted

the words out before she could have
second thoughts. She felt vindicated in
a way. After all, she had tried to revise
her price, and Luke Rivers would have
none of it. There seemed nothing
standing in the way of her taking the
job — other than the fact of what his
actions had led to eight years ago. Yet
Annie had thought she should do it,
and Annie was an honourable person.
So if she couldn't see anything
wrong . . .

Alex's brain raced as she planned
ahead. She would finish her current
job tomorrow and her other clients
wouldn't mind waiting a while, she was
sure. It shouldn't take more than a
couple of weeks, three at the most.
After that, she could banish Luke
Rivers from her mind and resume her
life as before. Neither Ricky nor
Lauren need ever know what she'd
done.

'I'll be there for eight thirty.'

5

Come Monday morning, at eight thirty precisely, Alex rang the doorbell of Grayling Manor. To her surprise, it was Luke Rivers himself who once again opened the door. With all of his wealth, she'd have expected him to have a housekeeper.

'Miss Harvey — oh, look, this is ridiculous. It's Alex, isn't it?'

'Yes.'

'And I'm Luke.'

'I know.'

He didn't seem at all bothered by her shortness of manner. 'Right. Well, come in, Alex.'

Alex smiled weakly and did as he bade. This wasn't how she'd planned things — to be on first-name terms with the enemy. Although she would be working for him, she'd intended to keep everything on a formal basis; distant, even. In just seconds, that resolve had been shot to pieces.

'I don't know where you want to start, but is there anything I can do for you or help you with? Maybe bring in your paint tins?'

'It's fine. I can manage.' Really, was he determined to put her off her stride? She'd never, not in her wildest dreams, envisaged Luke Rivers offering to carry her paint tins. Although maybe she should ask him to heave the step ladder over his shoulder? She'd make a bet he'd never had to do such a thing before. She smiled to herself.

'If you want to get off — ?' she murmured.

'There's no rush. I'll see you started first. Which room did you want to begin in?'

'I thought the dining room.'

He led her in and Alex saw that it had been completely cleared of what little furniture there had been. Had he done that? In the apparent absence of anyone else living in the house, it would seem likely.

'While I think of it, here's a key.' Luke held out his hand to her. 'Just in case I'm not always around when you come and go. I've had the burglar alarm disarmed, so you won't have to worry about that. I'll have a more up-to-date one fitted when I've refurnished. The damned thing kept going off at the most inconvenient times. In any case, there's not much here at the moment to steal. In fact, thieves would be welcome to most of it — It would save me the hassle of getting rid of it eventually.' He grinned at her.

He was starting to appear more and more likeable every time they met — something else that wasn't supposed to happen. 'If I'm not back before you want to leave, just lock the front door after you. What time do you work till? Just as a matter of interest.'

The question was casually asked, yet Alex had the impression that her answer mattered. 'It depends. If things are going well, I stay on. Of course, sometimes I reach a stage where I can't just down tools; a particular section has to be finished. I've been known to stay for as long as the light is good, if that's all right?' Which, as it was the middle of June, could mean anything up till about nine o'clock. She didn't know what time he worked until, but maybe he wouldn't want to find her still here when he returned.

'Fine by me.'

'Okay. I'll go get my things in.'

'If you're sure I can't help, I think I will go. My first appointment's at — ' He checked his watch. ' — nine thirty.'

★   ★   ★

Once he'd left, it didn't take Alex long to carry in her equipment. She didn't need that much, as she'd be mainly stripping wallpaper today.

By mid-afternoon, however, the walls of the dining room were ready for painting. The job was beginning to look like a breeze; Alex was confident she'd finish easily within the two weeks she'd allowed. She'd told Ricky he could go to Austria right after Luke had accepted her quote. His face had lit up.

'Wow! Cool! Thanks, Alex.'

'Yes, well, let's have a little less defiance from now on. And no lager-drinking, otherwise I might have to rethink.'

★ ★ ★

But things didn't go quite to plan. After the initial stripping of the wall, the work progressed extremely slowly. So slowly, in fact, that Alex's initial guilt at the amount she was charging Luke vanished. She'd never actually tried to frottage before and, although her efforts were successful, it was proving much more time-consuming than she'd envisaged. If she'd gone with her original costing, she would have seriously underpriced the job.

On this particular day, come six

o'clock, she had reached the point where she needed to leave the paint to dry, so she began to clear up. She'd almost finished when she heard the front door open.

'Hello, anyone in?'

It wasn't Luke's voice; in fact, she'd seen neither hide nor hair of him since the morning she'd started, and that was four days ago. She'd actually begun to wonder if he were avoiding her. Now she was startled and more than a little annoyed. He could have warned her that someone else other than herself had a key.

A man strode into the room — a man who was so like Luke to look at that he could only be his brother. He had the same swarthy skin, the same dark hair and eyes. He wasn't quite as tall as Luke, but — were they twins? She wondered. No, this man looked younger. And he didn't possess that same air of presence, of utter self-assurance, that Luke had. He was also much more friendly.

'Hi. You must be Alex.' He glanced in some amusement at the brightly coloured scarf tied peasant-fashion around her head.

Alex felt herself blushing. She was a messy painter and usually managed to get almost as much upon herself as whatever she was painting. She was quite sure that the scarf and probably her face were liberally speckled with the colour that she was putting onto the walls.

'I'm Scott, Luke's younger brother.' He held out a hand.

Alex wiped her one hand on her trousers before taking his. Not that it would do much good, as her trousers were almost as paint-stained as her hands were.

'I say.' He was looking around him for the first time. He seemed oblivious to the stickiness of her fingers. 'This is going to be really something.'

Pride surged through Alex, just as it did every time someone praised her efforts. 'Thank you,' she demurely murmured. 'I'm rather pleased with it myself.'

'I should think you are. Luke said you were good, but this is amazing.'

Alex's heart lurched. So Luke had said that, had he? She knew she shouldn't be, but she was warmed by his praise.

'I was looking for Luke. He's not back, clearly. We're supposed to be going out for dinner. I say,' he added, gazing at her, 'I don't suppose you'd like to join us?'

To say that Alex was taken aback by this unexpected invitation would be a masterpiece of understatement. 'Oh . . . I don't think so. I'm not dressed.' She indicated her stained jeans and her paint-speckled top.

The front door opened for a second time. It was Luke. He strode into the room and seemed surprised to see his brother. 'Hello, Alex. Scott.' His keen-eyed glance went straight to the headscarf, and the glint of amusement that Alex had seen now on a couple of occasions made its first appearance — along with the specks of gold. She was beginning to realise what it was they signified: suppressed laughter. He didn't make any reference to the scarf, however. Which, Alex decided, was a remarkable feat of self-control, given what she already knew of his propensity for sarcasm. Instead, he carried on addressing his brother. 'You're early, Scott. I hope he hasn't been getting in your way, Alex?'

Which was a strange thing to say. It was as if he were talking about a boy rather than a man. Alex saw Scott's expression alter from good-natured amicability to brooding resentment. He opened his mouth as if to say something.

'Oh, no,' Alex hastened to say, hoping to forestall any sort of argument. 'He's just been having a look at my work.'

'Well,' he said, glancing around, 'it's well worth looking at. I'm glad we opted for this finish. I've been monitor-ing your progress — it's going to transform the room. Well done, Alex.' And Luke strode across to her to take her one hand in both of his, a warm smile lifting the corners of his mouth.

His action caught her completely unawares. Alex could only pray that the quick clean she'd resorted to before taking Scott's hand had been sufficient. The last thing she wanted was to have her and Luke's fingers glued together.

Embarrassed now, she tried to free herself of his grasp, which proved more difficult than she'd anticipated. They weren't actually stuck together, but there was a distinctly treacly feel to things. She nibbled at her bottom lip, something she invariably did in moments of difficulty and, more firmly now, managed to tug her fingers free. 'S-sorry. The paint, you know.'

'Luke,' Scott began, seeming to have got over his vexation with his brother sufficiently to slip an arm around Alex's shoulders and give them a squeeze, 'I've asked Alex to join us this evening.'

'Thank you, Scott — ' Alex turned

her head to grin at the younger man. ' — It's very nice of you but really, I don't think — well, I'm not in any state to go anywhere. I mean, look at me.' She held both hands out in front of her, palms up, emphasising the fact that they were still liberally streaked with paint despite her efforts to wipe them.

But Scott didn't as much as glance at them; he was staring at her face instead — for all the world as if she had unexpectedly metamorphosed into something wonderful. It must have been her broad grin, she decided. She'd clearly overdone it, in an effort to compensate for her refusal of his invitation.

'Oh, come on, Alex. Luke won't mind. And, paint-covered or not, you can hold my hand any time.' And he laughed, uproariously.

His laughter was infectious and Alex found herself joining in. It was obvious that Scott liked her very much — in stark contrast to his brother, who was now regarding them both with what looked dangerously like displeasure.

'I didn't realise you two knew each other so well. How long have you been here, Scott?'

For all that Luke's words were smoothly spoken, there was a definite edge to them. Even his glance was weighted with disapproval.

A question sprang into Alex's mind. Did he not think her good enough to dine with them? Was that it? The idea angered her. She ought to go, if only to show the high-and-mighty Luke Rivers that she was every bit as refined as he was; that she knew how to behave at the table, which knife and fork to use, and how to hold her soup spoon at the correct angle. But her resolve wavered as she noted the way in which Luke was regarding his brother. His expression was ... challenging, she supposed would be an apt description.

'Just a few minutes. Um, he arrived just before you, actually.' It was Alex who spoke and she was gabbling, something else she invariably did whenever she was nervous.

'What's the matter, bro?' Scott said. 'Frightened I might have got one up on you?'

Alex stared at the younger man in horror. What on earth was Scott insinuating? That Luke was attracted to her and so was jealous over her? Ye Gods!

'Please come, Alex.' Scott had turned back to her, a look of pleading upon his face. 'We'll wait for you to go home and change — won't we, Luke?' He swung to his older brother. Alex couldn't see Luke's expression now; his face was turned away from her. Deliberately? she wondered.

'Of course.' Luke's tone had lost every scrap of its earlier warmth. In fact, it would have given an Arctic blizzard stiff competition. Whatever had happened to the likable person of a few days ago? He might never have existed. For he was clearly angered by his younger brother's persistence. And, even more clearly, he didn't want Alex dining with them.

Alex said the only thing she could think of under the circumstances. 'No, really, I don't think so.' Not for anything would she go where she wasn't wanted. She had too much pride for that.

But, unexpectedly, when he turned his head to look at her once more, Luke's expression was one of challenge again, and this time it was aimed squarely at her. 'Oh, come on, Alex. You'd be most welcome. Especially to Scott, clearly. Stop him getting bored with the tedious company of just his older brother.'

As Alex had never been one to refuse a challenge, almost before she had time to think, she heard herself saying, 'Okay. Thank you, I'd love to join you. I will go home and change, though.' She smiled with saccharine sweetness, at the same time wryly thinking, *So much for pride*. 'You know, swap the scarf for a clean one.' She ignored Scott's snigger of mirth and the tightening of Luke's lips at her display of ironical humour. 'And I'll be back here in — an, hour, shall we say?'

* * *

The first thing Alex did upon reaching home was to look in on Ricky who, for once, was in his bedroom doing his homework.

'I'm going back out. Is that okay? There's a pizza in the fridge for your tea.'

'Yeah. Cool! Where're you going?' He spoke without looking up from his book.

'I don't know.' She hadn't thought to ask. Damn. Now she wouldn't know what to wear. Casual or dressy? Maybe she'd plump for something halfway between.

'Who're you going with then?' Ricky did glance up this time.

'Uh . . . ' She didn't dare say Luke Rivers. Ricky would have a fit. She must have been crazy to agree. To be going out with Luke Rivers, of all people. Although she wasn't going out with him, not in the strictest sense of the word. There would be three of them, after all. Ricky never mentioned the name any more but Alex was sure that if she mentioned it now, he would remember precisely who Luke Rivers was. 'The client whose house I'm working in,' she finally said. She hated deceiving him, but what else could she do? And it wasn't actually a lie, was it? Just not the whole truth.

'Wow!' Ricky was full of admiration. 'Mixing in posh circles these days, eh? Isn't it Grayling Manor where you're working?'

'Yes, that's right. Look, I have to go and change.'

Any minute now he'd be asking who the owner of the house was. It was a wonder he didn't already know, come to think of it, seeing how local it was. But, she supposed, things like that didn't matter to a fifteen-year-old boy.

'Okay.' He turned his attention back

to his books. 'Have a nice time.'

'Thanks. Um, Ricky . . . '

'Yeah?'

'No drinking, remember.'

'Yeah, yeah. I'm going to the cinema. Is that okay?'

'Sure. But finish that homework first and don't be late back.'

He gave her a cheeky grin. 'Nah. Nor you.'

Alex walked over to him and ruffled his hair. He hated her doing that. Which was why she did it.

'Sis!' he predictably grumbled.

'Love you.' She dropped a kiss upon his head.

★   ★   ★

Half an hour later, Alex was dressed and putting the finishing touches to her freshly shampooed hair. After sorting through almost her entire wardrobe, she'd finally opted for a pair of cream linen trousers and a flame-coloured shirt, loosely belted so that it looked like a tunic. She turned this way and that, studying her reflection in the mirror. The soft fabric clung to her, outlining the shape of her breasts.

She sighed, not for the first time thinking what wouldn't she give for another couple of inches of fullness. Like Lauren. Had that been what had attracted Luke to her? If so, then he clearly liked his women voluptuous; shapely. Well, that should effectively save her, Alex, from any unwelcome attentions. Modestly curved, she might be; voluptuous, she was not.

She slipped her feet into a pair of cream wedges, dabbed on some of her favourite perfume and left the room. He'd have to take her as she was. She grinned at her involuntary phrasing. She couldn't imagine Luke Rivers *taking* her at all.

She climbed into her van and started the engine. She'd had no more problems since having the new battery fitted so, within minutes, she was parking it in front of Grayling Manor. It was Luke who greeted her at the door.

'That was quick.' His smile didn't quite reach his eyes. 'And to achieve such results in so little time is nothing short of a miracle.'

'Thank you.' She wasn't sure whether that was a compliment or not. Surely she hadn't looked so bad that it would take hours of work to improve things?

'Scott, Alex is here. Please come in, Alex.'

As Alex followed him into the house, she had to struggle to hide her dismay. He was effectively pairing her with Scott. Although why that should dismay her so, she didn't know. She'd already worked out for herself that she wasn't Luke's type.

6

Alex didn't know how, but she managed to get through the evening without revealing her feelings about the man sitting opposite her.

She sat with Scott on one side of the table in one of the smartest restaurants in the area; Luke faced them. This arrangement had been at Luke's suggestion.

'So,' Scott drawled towards the end of the evening. Conversation before this had been pretty general; there'd been no further sign of the conflict that Alex had sensed between the brothers earlier. 'Why haven't I seen you around before this, Alex? Do you ever come to Dorrington? I've got an apartment there. We could meet up — have a meal, a drink.'

'I don't go out much in the evenings,' Alex told him. 'I have a younger brother to keep an eye on, and then there's my work.'

'But what about your parents? Don't they look after your brother?'

Alex was vexed at not having anticipated just such a question and for a moment was at a loss as to how to answer. If she told them the story of her parents' deaths, would Luke remember and fit the pieces together? He must have known what happened in the aftermath of his break-up with Lauren, mustn't he?

For the first time then, it occurred to her that maybe he didn't. Lauren would have been unlikely to have stayed in contact with the man who'd so brutally and abruptly ended their relationship. It felt like the ultimate crime to Alex — that he should have been the indirect cause of the deaths of two people and hadn't even known it.

For a split second, she was tempted to tell Scott the truth and see how Luke reacted. But that would be foolish: cutting off her nose to spite her face.

Because for all she knew he might feel so bad about it, he wouldn't want her around any longer.

She'd keep quiet for now.

Maybe when she'd finished the job, then she'd tell him the truth? Tell him how his callous action had culminated in her parents' deaths. But not now. Not when she was banking on the money he'd be paying her, to fund Ricky's school trip if nothing else.

So, with all of this in mind, she prevaricated; was deliberately vague. 'No, they're — um, they're both dead.' Even now, she couldn't say it without a tremble in her voice.

Scott obviously heard it because he laid a hand over hers, squeezing it comfortingly. 'I'm sorry,' he murmured.

The conversation ground to an uncomfortable halt and, belatedly, she was aware of Luke watching her. Was he going to ask her how they died? And if she told him, and he did indeed know what had happened, would he make the connection? But all he said was, 'I'm so sorry, Alex. How have you managed alone?' He looked genuinely concerned now. Pity he couldn't have shown the same sort of concern for Lauren, she grimly reflected.

'By working hard to support us both.'

'How old is your brother?'

'Fifteen.'

'Oh dear. The most difficult age.' He grinned ruefully. 'There's no one as troublesome as a teenage boy. I recall my own teens, and Scott's. Although, as I recall, Scott's difficult period well outlasted his teens.' His expression as he regarded his brother was a strange one, almost accusing. Alex wondered what Scott had done to merit such a look.

'Yeah, yeah, all right, bro. Not here, okay?' Scott looked annoyed and — yes, embarrassed. Alex was intrigued.

'What's your brother's name?' This was from Luke once again. He seemed inordinately interested in Alex's background. Alex shifted uneasily in her seat. Not for the first time that evening, she wished she'd stayed at home.

'Ri-Richard.' Alex gave him her brother's full name. After all, she couldn't be sure that Lauren wouldn't have mentioned her young cousin.

'He must miss your parents.' This came from Scott. His hand was still over hers on the table and now he'd started to caress her fingers.

Alex felt distinctly uncomfortable. Luke's eyes had darkened — with disapproval? she wondered. Yet, it had been he who had placed her and Scott side by side. She tugged her hand away. Scott gave a rueful smile.

She was beginning to feel like a rag doll, being pulled this way and that between the brothers.

'How old were you when you lost your parents?' Luke asked.

The frigid coldness of earlier that evening had vanished; now, he was warmly interested in her. The man possessed all the characteristics of a chameleon, she decided irritably, seemingly able to change mood in the blink of an eyelid.

'Twenty-one,' she said. 'Old enough to take care of Richard, thankfully. Otherwise I'm sure he'd have been taken away from me. Anyway, talking of Richard,' she said, glancing at her watch, 'it's time I left.'

The two men got to their feet and Luke said, 'I'll see you to your van.'

She'd driven herself to the restaurant, thinking it would be easier than having to return to the manor to pick her van up, and now she gave heartfelt thanks that she had had that foresight. She couldn't have borne another second of their probing questions. Remaining on her guard, having to think about everything she said, was proving more of a strain than she'd anticipated. Suddenly, she longed to be at home in her dressing gown, a mug of cocoa in her hand.

'It's all right, bro',' Scott put in, 'I'll do that.'

'No, here's some money. You stay and settle the bill. I'll see you outside.'

Luke placed a hand beneath Alex's

elbow and shepherded her from the restaurant. Alex's heart raced until she thought it was about to burst from her chest.

'I can get myself back to my van, you know,' she nervously began. 'There's no need — '

'Yes, there is. I want to make sure it starts, for one thing.'

'It will.' Her voice quivered. The last person she wanted to be alone with was Luke Rivers. Yet, what was she frightened of? She didn't know.

Her own feelings, maybe?

For Luke Rivers, on the whole, was turning out to be the exact opposite of everything she'd expected. She could see now why Lauren had fallen so heavily for him. Was that what she was scared of? That she'd do the same? 'I've had a new battery fitted,' she managed to say.

'I know, but for my own peace of mind.'

Alex could do nothing else but go with him. Silently, they walked to her van. It looked hopelessly out of place amongst all the expensive cars that were sitting on the car park. She grimaced to herself. It was a wonder the owners of the restaurant hadn't asked her to move it. It didn't fit the image they must wish to promote if the look of the other obviously wealthy diners had been anything to go by.

'I just wanted to say,' Luke said suddenly, 'how pleased I am with your work so far and to ask — ' He seemed to hesitate, as if unsure how to go on, ' — as you haven't demanded a deposit or any money up front, if you wanted some . . . help with expenses? I appreciate things must be difficult for you.'

'Oh.' Yet again, he'd caught her by surprise. 'Well, I wouldn't say no.'

'Good. Shall we say half up front then?'

'Oh — I wasn't thinking of that much.'

'No? Well, I was. I'll leave the cheque for you at the house. Or, if I'm still there, I'll give it to you, obviously.'

Alex nodded. Again, she thought, this wasn't the man Lauren had described. A heartless philanderer had been her cousin's depiction of him. But to be fair, that was eight years ago, and people did change. Maybe Annie was right and she should let go of her anger? Maybe it was time to move on?

'And just for the record,' he was saying now, 'I think you've been very courageous, coping like you have.'

'Thank you, Luke.' Even she could discern the astonishment in her tone, so surely Luke must be able to. If he did, however, he gave no indication of it.

'And — about Scott.' Aah, could this be the real reason he'd escorted her to her van? 'He gets carried away where women — especially attractive ones — are concerned. I wouldn't want to see you get hurt.'

Irritation swept over Alex in the wake of his warning, transforming her opinion of him once again. He was a one to talk, after the way he'd treated Lauren.

'I'm a twenty-nine-year-old woman, Luke,' she snapped, 'not a naïve nineteen-year-old — ' She bit her bottom lip. Why in heaven's name had she said that? Would he remember that Lauren had been only nineteen? She must have spoken about her cousins, and if she had mentioned the name Harvey, could it just be enough to jog Luke's memory? 'Don't worry about me. I've learnt to take care of myself, I can assure you. I've had to, after all.' Her tone was brusque.

Why, oh why had she started this deception? Why didn't she just tell him the truth right now, and take whatever the consequences might be? If she lost the job, she lost it. She'd have to find the money for Ricky's trip from somewhere else. But something stopped her; she didn't know what. Maybe the thought of her brother's disappointment if she couldn't come up with the money?

'I'm sorry if I've offended you,' Luke said.

Alex didn't answer.

'I didn't mean — ' His face had darkened, as had his eyes.

'What did you mean, Luke? That you don't think I'm good enough for a brother of yours?'

What was wrong with her? Why didn't she just leave things? Why did she have to go on gnawing at something? She was grossly overreacting. All the result, she knew, of his behaviour eight years ago. It had been unforgivable. No, despite what Annie had said and what she herself had been feeling just seconds ago, she couldn't forget what he'd done, or forgive it.

Luke was staring at her as if she'd taken leave of her senses. Which, she supposed, in a way she had. 'No, of course I don't think that. I was merely trying to warn you. Scott's — well, he can be rather immature, that's all.'

'Yes, well, we can all be that at times, can't we, Luke? So don't worry. Now if you've finished, I'll say goodnight and I'll see you, or not, in the morning.' She was trembling so badly by this time that, when she pulled out her key to unlock the van door, she instantly dropped it. It clattered noisily onto the ground.

Luke bent and retrieved it. 'Let me,' he said, and he deftly unlocked the door. He turned to her then. 'Alex, I'm sorry if I've upset you. I certainly don't think you're not good enough for Scott. Rather the reverse, actually.' His head was awfully close to hers now; so close she could smell his aftershave. It filled her nostrils and her head, making it swim. She felt herself sway. Luke immediately put an arm about her to steady her.

'Alex — ?' His voice was husky all of a sudden; throaty.

Alex couldn't believe what was happening when he lowered his head to hers. Her breath caught in her throat and, in the next second, his lips were brushing her cheek, seeking out the corner of her mouth. Her heart went into hyperdrive.

'Luke? Where are you? Is Alex still there?' It was Scott.

Alex tore herself from Luke's grasp, not daring to look up at him. Instead, she wrenched open the door of her van and dove almost headlong inside just as Scott loomed into view, an anxious expression upon his face.

'Good, you're still here. I wanted to say goodnight. And — and to say that I'd like to see you again.'

Alex did manage a smile, albeit a shaky one. She couldn't believe this. Both brothers were coming on to her. It didn't help her state of mind when Scott took her smile as a sign of encouragement and leant in the van towards her. If he kissed her as well — ?

Alex did the only thing she could think of: she turned her head away. 'Oh, I'm sure you will, Scott. I'm working for your brother, after all.'

'I didn't mean that, Alex.'

'No?' Alex groped for the ignition key. It wasn't there. Wildly, she looked around for it. She had to get away.

Luke calmly dangled it in front of her. 'This what you're looking for?' Something glinted in his eye. It could have been amusement, or it could have been — what? Anger? Disappointment? She didn't know, and she didn't want to. She just wanted to get home, to leave these warring brothers behind. She refused to consider that the object of their warfare might be her.

'Oh, um, yes. Uh, thanks and um, thank you for a lovely evening.' She thrust the key in the ignition.

'You can't go just like that. Give me your phone number,' Scott was saying. 'I'll ring you. We'll go out, just you and I.'

'I've got her number, Scott.' Luke's voice was low, almost contemptuous.

'Oh, yes — of course. I'll be in touch,' Scott promised as she started the engine and finally pulled away. She just wanted to get back to Ricky — to normality.

But the house, she discovered when

she got there, was in complete darkness, and empty. Alex frowned. It was gone eleven. Where was Ricky?

Then, just as worry over her brother began to drive everything else from her mind, the front door opened and he lurched in.

7

'For heaven's sake, Ricky,' Alex cried, 'where have you been? I thought you were going to the cinema?'

'I did,' he mumbled, 'but then I went to the pub.' He'd obviously been drinking.

'Which one?' Alex asked, aghast. 'I'll report the publican for serving under-age boys.'

'Wasn't me he served.' He giggled. 'Nigel bought it and he's over eighteen. So thass okay, isn't it?'

'Nigel? Who the devil's Nigel? Was he one of the boys who were here with you the other evening?'

'Yeah.' He moved closer and nearly knocked her out with the lager fumes. 'He-he's a g-good mate.'

'He's not a mate of any sort to get you into this state.'

'Oh, don't start. I'm not a child any

longer. We all drink lager nowadays.'

'Go to bed, Ricky. We'll discuss this in the morning when you've sobered up.'

As promised, she confronted him over breakfast the next morning. 'I want you to stop seeing this Nigel. He's obviously a bad influence.'

'Honestly, all this fuss over a couple of lagers. You're not my mother, you know. Anyway, you'd have plenty to moan about if I was up to the sort of things some of the others are.' He stopped short, as if aware that he'd said too much.

A feeling of dread assailed Alex. 'So what's that then?'

'Oh, a bit of thieving, you know. Shoplifting. I don't do that; you should be grateful instead — instead of constantly whingeing.' And with that, he got up from the table. 'I'm going to school to get some peace.'

Once he'd left Alex sat, her head bowed in her hands. Maybe he was right. Lager was a whole lot less serious than theft. She'd have another go at talking to him this evening. Try to make him see that it was better to do neither.

★ ★ ★

She was deliberately later than usual arriving at Grayling Manor, hoping that Luke would have already left. She really didn't feel up to facing him after what had happened the night before. A kiss, as fleeting as it was, had been the last thing she had expected. And she certainly didn't need that sort of complication. She sighed. All in all, it would be a great deal simpler if he wasn't at home.

But he was, and judging by the expression upon his face, he had been waiting for her.

'H-hello,' she haltingly said. 'I thought you'd be gone by now.'

'Did you?' His tone was a dispassionate one, leading Alex to wonder if she was making too much of what had, after all, been no more than a fleeting caress.

'I-I had a few things to pick up on my way here. That's why I'm late.' Which wasn't exactly a lie; she had stopped to buy a newspaper and a sandwich for her lunch.

'I thought I'd wait and give you this personally, after our conversation last night.' He held out a piece of paper. It was a cheque. 'And I want to apologise.' He couldn't seem to look at her as he spoke.

Alex was confused. This . . . trepidation, for want of a better word, didn't at all fit her image of him.

'For last night,' he went on. 'I shouldn't have — '

She didn't let him finish. 'Oh, you mean the kiss. Well, it wasn't really a kiss, was it?' She laughed lightly. 'Think no more of it. I've already forgotten it. We all do foolish things after a drink.' Somehow — she didn't know how — she mustered up a breezy smile.

Luke didn't return it. In fact, he

didn't do anything for a long moment. He simply stared at her before saying, 'Actually, I wasn't going to apologise for that. And, as you so rightly say, it wasn't really a kiss, but just for the record, it also wasn't the result of a drink. Far from it, as I was driving; if you recall, I'd been on mineral water throughout. As I believe you were.' His smile was a tight-lipped one. 'So, I was going to apologise for trying to tell you who you should see and not see. But if that's the way you want to play things,' he added as he shrugged, 'then so be it.'

Inexplicably, Alex felt chastened and rebuffed as he turned away from her and picked up his briefcase. She thought she heard him murmur, 'However, I'm not so sure it will be that easily forgotten,' but decided, upon his swinging to face her once more, his face looking as if it had been chiselled out of a block of marble, that she must be mistaken.

★　★　★

Once he'd gone, Alex went into the dining room, intending to begin work. But something about that morning's encounter — as brief as it had been — had her restlessly prowling around the other ground-floor rooms. Maybe if she saw the way he lived, the things he surrounded himself with, she'd get a better idea of what made Luke Rivers tick. At the moment he was a total enigma.

As she'd already seen the drawing room, and it was empty anyway, she pushed open one of the other doors that led off the hallway. She'd also been a frequent visitor to the kitchen, having made herself cups of coffee on a fairly regular basis, so she didn't bother with that either.

Instead, she opened another door and found herself in what she believed was called a 'snug' nowadays: a smaller, cosier sitting room than the large drawing room. By the look of the comfortable arm-chairs and settee, as well as the crammed bookcase, flat-screen television set, DVD and CD players, it was obvious that this was where Luke spent his spare time. She pushed the eject button on the CD player and looked at the name on the disc. Vivaldi's *Four Seasons*. It was one of her favourites too.

She left that room and went into the next one. This was used as an office, judging by the large desk and laptop computer. There was also a television set and DVD player in here.

Feeling vaguely disappointed, she returned to the hall. There'd been nothing personal, apart from books and CDs, in any of the rooms. Nothing to give her much of a clue to the real man.

She glanced up the stairs. No, she couldn't. That would be a real intrusion — wouldn't it? She took the stairs, two at a time. Guiltily, she tried all the doors. There were five of them. One room held the things Luke had moved from the dining room and lounge, and the last one opened into what was clearly Luke's bedroom. She didn't go in, but just stood in the doorway looking at the vast bed, the twin wardrobes, the dressing table, another television and DVD player — still nothing of a personal nature, except for a photograph. It was of an elderly couple laughing into the camera lens. His parents? she wondered.

But that was it. No photos of a girlfriend, or friends; nothing. She returned downstairs no wiser than when she'd begun the tour of inspection.

★　★　★

Alex had been working for over an hour when she heard the sound of the front door opening.

'Alex?'

It was Scott. He strode into the room. 'Thought I'd surprise you.' He grinned engagingly at her.

Alex smiled at him. 'You've done that all right.'

'I came to ask you out.'

'I thought you were going to phone

me,' she murmured.

'I thought a personal invitation would carry more weight.'

'Don't you have a job to go to?' It was only ten thirty in the morning. He must either have taken the time off, or he had a very lenient boss. Of course, she supposed he could work for himself — like her?

'No, I'm between jobs at the moment.'

'Oh? What did you do?'

He looked away from her, and his expression an evasive one. 'Oh, you know, a bit of this and that.'

'I thought you might have worked for Luke?'

He snorted. 'Tried that. Decided I'd rather work for the Devil himself; he'd be a damn sight easier to please.' He paused, as if trying to decide whether to go on or not. 'Luke and I don't exactly see eye to eye, as you probably guessed from last night.'

'Well, I did.'

'He treats me like a child still,' he

suddenly burst out. 'So, he certainly wouldn't trust me with a position of any importance in one of his precious businesses. It's much easier to fob me off with an allowance. Gets me out of his hair that way.'

Alex had to hide a smile. It didn't sound as if he was suffering too much hardship. 'Well, maybe you should try and make him see you as an adult and then he might change his mind.' She recalled his sulky expression from the previous evening towards his older brother. Mind you, Luke had spoken as if he were still a boy, so perhaps Scott had good reason to complain, allowance or no allowance.

'Do you think I haven't tried?' he exclaimed. 'No, it's all because — ' He stopped talking abruptly and a strange look came over his face. A look of almost . . . triumph.

'Because what, Scott?' Alex gently asked.

'Nothing,' Scott muttered. 'Anyway, that's enough about Luke. It's us I came to discuss, not my tyrant of a brother. But be warned, Alex; he doesn't forgive easily. You step out of line just once and — ' He slashed a finger across his throat. ' — you're dead. You may as well not exist any longer for Luke.'

It occurred then to Alex that that could have been what had happened to Lauren. For the first time, and given what she now knew of Luke, she wondered whether Lauren had done something that Luke just hadn't been able to forgive?

'Anyway.' Scott was smiling again, his frown gone, Luke obviously completely forgotten. 'Will you come out with me?'

'I don't see why not.'

'Really? You will?'

'Yes, I'd like that.'

He was like a small boy, Alex decided in that moment, standing beaming at her for all the world as if she'd offered him a special treat. Maybe Luke could be forgiven for regarding him in such a light.

But that aside, it had been so long since she'd been taken out by a man, just the two of them, that she suspected she'd be totally out of practice as far as the business of flirting went. She'd been so involved in her job and raising Ricky, and then her efforts to get Something Special up and running, that she'd had no time for any sort of romantic entanglement.

She picked up a cloth and concentrated on wiping her sticky fingers, which was why she didn't notice Scott moving closer.

'I'm very attracted to you, Alex.'

His voice was low and right by the side of her. Alex, too, spoke softly. 'I know.'

'Cocky, huh?' He grinned at her. 'Mind you, I suppose you've good reason to be. A beautiful woman like you.'

Alex couldn't help but laugh at that. 'Let's not exaggerate, Scott.'

'Who's exaggerating?' Scott murmured. 'That's why Luke is attracted to you.'

'Luke? Attracted to me?' she scoffed. She couldn't think of anything more unlikely — yet he had kissed her, or tried to. And she couldn't help but wonder what would have happened if Scott hadn't interrupted.

'Oh yes.' Scott looked the picture of confidence. 'It's usually Luke who gets the beautiful women.' His smile was a smug one. 'So maybe I can beat him to it this time, instead of always coming second best.' He slipped an arm about Alex's waist.

She didn't ask him what he meant by that remark; she was far too busy trying to work out whether he could be right in his assumption.

'Kiss me, Alex,' he murmured. 'Ple-ease.'

Once again, he reminded her of a small boy. A dangerously appealing small boy at that. Which could be why Alex allowed her guard to slip; to think well, why not? He was attractive, after all. And one kiss was hardly likely to change the world. It might, however, drive the memory of Luke and his disturbing caress from her head.

She lifted her face to his. Scott sighed and placed his mouth upon hers.

The kiss started off lightly, no more than a mere brush of lips. Which, instead of banishing the memory of Luke from Alex's mind, brought everything back in minute detail. She waited, the breath catching in her throat, for a similar response to the one she'd had then.

There was nothing.

As if Scott sensed her lack of feeling, he deepened the kiss, prising her mouth apart to slide his tongue inside. Alex felt the beginnings of revulsion. She started to pull away.

'What the hell is going on here?'

She and Scott sprang apart and turned as one to see Luke standing there, his eyes blazing with anger, his mouth tightened into an uncompromising line.

8

'Luke!'

Despite his exclamation of surprise, Scott didn't look in the least bit put out by his brother's unexpected appearance; in fact, he appeared pleased if anything — as distinct from Alex, who was deeply embarrassed and blushing hotly. At the same time, she couldn't help questioning Scott's motives in asking her out, in kissing her. Had he planned this? Could he have known that Luke would appear?

But Scott's next question seemed to disprove that theory. Because, belatedly and visibly irritated, he snapped, 'What are you doing back, bro? Checking up on us?'

'Well, as I had no idea you'd be here, Scott, I would say that's unlikely, wouldn't you? No, I forgot something — fortuitously, as it turns out. Let's get one thing straight, Scott: I'm paying Alex to work, not make love with you. Now, please go.'

'We weren't making love!' Alex hotly protested.

Luke turned his smouldering gaze to her. Alex felt herself flinching. 'Oh, were you not?' In stark contrast to the look in his eye, his tone was ice-cool. 'Then, enlighten me. What would you call what you were doing, exactly?'

At first when Alex opened her mouth, nothing came out. Then, 'Um, just . . . just . . . '

She turned her head just in time to see Scott sidling from the room, obviously set on abandoning her to the mercies of this — this heartless monster. A monster, moreover, who was regarding her as if she were something he'd picked up on the sole of his shoe. Was this how he'd looked at Lauren when he'd ended things? If he had, feeling about him as she did, it was no wonder she'd considered suicide.

'Well?'

Alex turned to face Luke. The gold glints had appeared in his eye. So they didn't just signify amusement, then. They also indicated contempt. 'We were just — um, flirting a little.'

His gaze hardened, as did his jaw line. 'As I said, I don't pay you to flirt — not even a little — with my brother.'

'Just who do you think you are?' she burst out.

'The man whose house you're in.' His tone flayed her. 'Now, as I tried to tell you before, stay away from Scott.' And without another word, he too turned and strode from the room.

★ ★ ★

It was in the middle of the afternoon, a couple of days later, when Alex's mobile phone rang. It was Annie. She'd been the only person that Alex had told about working for Luke.

'Hi, how's it going?' she now asked.

'Fine.' Even to Alex's own ears, her tone was abrupt. She was still smarting from Luke's tongue-lashing of her and Scott, and that was in spite of the fact that she'd seen nothing of him since. It had occurred to her that, in the wake of his outburst, maybe he was as reluctant to come face to face with her as she was with him? Yet he always seemed so sure of himself, that it did seem more than a little unlikely.

'I'd love to come and see what you've done so far. Do you think Luke Rivers would mind?'

'I shouldn't think so. Anyway, he's not here.'

'Great. I'll be with you in ten minutes.'

And she was.

'This is fantastic, Alex,' she enthused. 'You clever ol' thing. If he doesn't give you more work, I'll be amazed.'

'Thank you.' Alex just wished she could share Annie's optimism. But she had a strong suspicion that once she'd completed this job, Luke would have no desire to see her again — ever. Given the scene he'd interrupted between her and Scott, she was quite sure she'd well and truly blotted her copybook in his eyes, with no possible hope of redemption.

They both heard the sound of a key turning in the front door. 'Oh no,' hissed Annie. 'Is it the great man himself?'

'It seems a reasonable assumption, as he lives here.'

Oh God! He'd caught her again. This time, with someone in the house who shouldn't have been there.

'Look, maybe you should go, Annie.' Her heart thudded; her pulses raced. Which would account for the fact that, as Luke strode into the room, Alex's cheeks were literally aflame with embarrassment.

'Don't let me stop you.' His tone was just short of frigid, as was his look. 'Just thought I'd work from home this afternoon. Hello.' He was looking at Annie. 'Come to help Alex, have you? I wondered whose car it was outside.'

'Um — ' Alex began to stammer, 'no,

not help. This is my best friend, Annie. I hope you don't mind but she was interested in seeing the frottage effect. She's thinking of having it done in her house.'

Annie cocked an eyebrow at Alex and whispered, 'Quick thinkin', gal.'

'Oh, I see. In that case, pleased to meet you, Annie, and no, I don't mind. Far from it, actually.' As if to reinforce this sentiment, Luke was now openly and appreciatively appraising Annie. 'Luke Rivers.' He thrust a hand at her.

'Yes, I know.' Annie swiftly took it, returning his gaze with an equal amount of appreciation. A small smile began to play around her mouth as her eyelids lowered over gleaming eyes.

Alex's heart performed a steep-nose dive. She knew that look of Annie's only too well. It meant Annie liked what she saw and was set to indulge herself with a spot of harmless flirtation. It didn't signify a betrayal of Rob; it was simply that faced with a good-looking man — as Luke Rivers undeniably was — Annie couldn't help herself. It never led to anything, so Alex decided to let her get on with it. She was intrigued, in spite of herself, as to how Luke would respond.

'I've heard all about you,' Annie murmured provocatively.

'Have you now? So what have you heard, exactly?' The corners of Luke's mouth twitched with obvious amusement.

'Oh, you know.' Annie airily waved a hand. 'What a fantastic businessman you are. How many different pies you've . . . plunged your fingers into.'

How was it that Annie could make the simplest words sound — well, not to put too fine a point on it — erotic? Alex wondered.

'Go on.' Luke's smile was broad now. He wasn't at all put out by Annie's suggestiveness. In fact, he was enjoying himself. Alex could see that as plain as the nose on his face.

'Well, you're a self-made man,

extre-emely rich.' Annie smiled again, even more provocatively this time, resting her hands upon her hips, and thrusting her generously proportioned breasts forward.

Luke threw his head back and gave a shout of laughter.

'Women like you — and I can see why, now that I've met you.' She was practically purring.

Alex closed her eyes in helpless exasperation — in total contrast to Luke, she realised upon opening them again. He had merely tilted his head to one side, the better to view Annie apparently. He was in no way embarrassed by her bold statements. In fact, he was making the most of the attractive display presented to him. Alex watched as his gaze roamed lazily over her friend — until, in the end, she was forced to look away, the warmth now smouldering in his eyes belatedly unbearable.

A stab of jealousy shook her. He'd never looked at her like that. Mind you, why would he? She didn't possess the sort of assets that Annie did. Misery washed over her at her own inadequacies, making her snap, 'Annie, you'll embarrass Luke.'

Luke turned his gaze to her. It was gleaming with — what? She couldn't identify the emotion. 'Oh, it would take more than that to embarrass me, Alex,' he drawled.

It crossed her mind that he was deliberately tantalising her, tormenting her, toying with her emotions. But why would he do that? Unless it was to hurt her? To punish her for her careless dismissal of his kiss — as fleeting a caress as it had been? Was that what he was doing? Or was he punishing her for kissing Scott the other day? She frowned and turned away from his suddenly darkened face.

'I'm sure it would,' murmured Annie.

'Tell me, are you, um, involved with anyone, Annie?' he asked.

Alex darted a horrified look at him. Did that mean what it sounded like?

Was he actually making a move on Annie?

'Well yes, actually, I am — sadly,' she saucily added. Alex swung just in time to see her pulling an exaggeratedly mournful face. 'Not that I don't love him dearly, mind. I do. It's just that I can't resist a handsome man; I just have to flirt a little. It's a particular failing of mine.' And she gazed guilelessly up at him.

Luke again laughed. It was a warm sound; beguiling, even. Well, she'd got what she wanted, Alex decided. She'd gone out of her way to try and discover the personal side of Luke Rivers, and that was exactly what she was now getting. The trouble was, Alex didn't like what she was seeing, not one little bit. He'd never laughed like this with her; not that she'd given him reason to, she supposed. Theirs was, after all, purely a business arrangement. Still . . .

'Isn't it time you went, Annie?' she pointedly asked.

'Whoops.' Annie grinned cheekily at

her. 'I do believe I'm treading on someone's toes.'

'Annie,' Alex grimly warned, at the same time grabbing her friend by the arm and all but pushing her into the hall and towards the front door.

'Okay, okay, I'm going.' Annie smiled over her shoulder at a still grinning Luke; he'd followed them out. 'Maybe we can do this again sometime? Make up a foursome?' she finished hopefully.

Alex opened the front door and literally shoved her outside.

'What do you think you're doing?' Alex demanded once they were outside and out of Luke's hearing. 'Whatever would Rob think? He trusts you.'

Annie looked wounded for a second. 'I was only having some fun. Rob would know that's all it was. He's used to my little ways.' She paused, eyeing Alex reflectively. 'Luke seems okay, Alex.' She paused again. 'Are you sure it was him that Lauren was seeing? Only — '

'Of course it was him. How many other Luke Riverses do you know of?'

Annie shrugged. 'None, but — '

'It was him, take it from me. And for you to flirt with him like that? Well, it was outrageous, Annie. And what's he going to make of that little remark? 'Whoops, I'm stepping on someone's toes', for heaven's sake? Honestly, I could kill you at times.'

Annie was staring at her, every bit as guilelessly as she'd stared at Luke. 'You're jealous, Alex Harvey.'

'Don't be ridiculous,' she cried. 'Me, jealous? Of you and Luke Rivers? Puhleese.'

But Annie wasn't looking at her anymore; she was staring over Alex's shoulder. Alex glanced back as well — and promptly closed her eyes in mortified anguish.

Luke Rivers himself.

How long had he been standing there? And more to the point, how much of that had he heard?

'Everything okay?' he smoothly asked.

'Yes, fine.' Annie fluttered a hand at

him as she headed for her car. 'I'm just going back to Rob.' Before she climbed into her car, she turned to Alex and said, 'Let's meet for a drink this evening, Alex. The Red Lion? Seven thirty?' She then glanced beyond Alex to Luke, who was still standing there, and said, 'See you again, hopefully. Bye for now.'

'Bye.' All traces of Luke's former amusement had disappeared by the time Alex turned around. His face now was set and implacable. Accusing, even?

'Alex, if you've got a moment?'

9

'Just coming.' Alex darted across to Annie. 'If he heard any of that,' she hissed, 'well, I will hold you fully responsible. I am not jealous, do you hear?'

'I hear.' Annie held up both arms in mock surrender. 'But if you take my advice, go for it.'

'Go for it? Go for what?'

'Luke, you muppet. He's too nice to have done what Lauren said. There's more to it all than she's told you, I'd stake my life on that. You don't think she could have been lying, do you?'

After Scott's remark about Luke's unforgiving nature, Alex had already wondered whether Lauren had done something bad enough to induce Luke to end their relationship. What she had never before considered was that Lauren might have been lying. But why would she have? It didn't make sense. Other than to paint Luke in the worst possible light and herself as the hapless victim. And what possible reason could she have had for doing that?

Alex walked back into the house, her heart rate twice as fast as it should have been. What did Luke want? Had he overheard their rash words and decided to get rid of her forthwith?

She strode into the dining room, mentally bracing herself for the worst.

'Aah, there you are.' His expression had reverted to normal, although there was a disconcerting gleam in his eye. Alex's heart fluttered uncomfortably as she wondered exactly how much he'd overheard outside.

'I wanted to ask for your help.' His smile now was one of undiluted and wildly engaging charm.

The quite remarkable transformation from accusing implacability to this was enough to induce Alex to blink rather rapidly and then say, somewhat rashly, 'Of course, anything I can do.'

'I need to go shopping for some things to fill the spaces. All I have is what I bought from the Gladwyns. Even the portraits were theirs — no room for them in their new bungalow, apparently. Mind you, looking at them, I can understand why they left them behind,' he dryly remarked. 'Not the most attractive people.'

'But you must have had furniture in your previous place, surely? Why didn't you bring that?'

'It's all too modern for this house.' He grinned ruefully, catapulting Alex's pulse into hyperdrive. 'Apart from the televisions, stereo stuff and computers, which I wanted to keep, I sold the flat lock, stock and barrel. I wanted a fresh start.' He paused. 'I wondered if you'd accompany me; advise me.'

'Me?' She didn't bother hiding her astonishment.

'Yes. The place needs a woman's touch.'

'Well, I mean . . . Isn't there someone else you could ask?' She only just stopped herself from adding, 'A girl-friend, perhaps?'

'We-ell, yes.' He paused. 'But not someone I would trust to advise me.'

That sounded as if he had a girlfriend, which would seem to shatter Scott's theory that he was attracted to Alex into several zillion pieces. If that were the case, why would he be interested in Alex? Yet if there was someone, somewhere, in the picture, why had she never been to the house? Unless, of course, she arrived after Alex had left each day?

'It's you I want.'

It would be so easy to misinterpret those simple words, Alex mused. Was that what he intended? Was he playing with her? Enacting some sort of cat and mouse game with her taking the part of the mouse, naturally? Once again, she wondered if he was punishing her for what he'd interpreted as her love-making with Scott.

'You're the professional,' he elabo-rated.

'Not really. I just decorate the rooms, not furnish them. And I really don't have the time. Not if you want this finished as quickly as possible.'

'Oh,' he began, brushing aside her reservations, 'one day won't make any difference. Will it?' He tilted his head to one side and watched her from beneath hooded lids. It was an engaging gesture and, once again, one she found she couldn't resist.

'Okay. When?'

'Tomorrow. I know it's Saturday, but — '

'No, I was planning to work anyway; I usually do.'

'Excellent. I'll even treat you to a meal.'

'There's no need,' she protested. The notion of a meal alone with Luke Rivers was enough to bring on palpitations. It had been bad enough in a threesome. At times she'd felt as if she were the victim of an inquisition. It could be even worse with just the two of them.

'I think there is. You'll be doing me a huge favour. I intend repaying it.'

* * *

That evening, just as they'd arranged, Alex met Annie at the Red Lion, a pub in the centre of Kingston Prior.

'Over here.' Annie waved as she walked in. 'I've got you a glass of wine. Hope that's okay?'

'Fine.' Alex sat down and lifted the glass to her lips. 'It's just what I need actually.' She took a large mouthful.

'Bad day?' Annie asked, her expression one of mischievous expectation. 'So, what happened after I left? Had he overheard us?'

Alex eyed her quizzically. Had she said those things deliberately, hoping Luke would hear them? No, Annie wouldn't do that . . . would she?

'Lord knows! Luke Rivers doesn't give much away.' She eyed her friend. After her suspicions of a moment ago, she found herself wondering how much she should tell Annie. She didn't want her blurting anything else out in front of Luke in the event that they should meet again. But was that likely? Oh, what the hell. Annie was her best friend. If she couldn't confide in her, who could she confide in?

'Scott, Luke's brother, thinks that Luke's attracted to me.'

'Does he?' Annie's expression now gave nothing away.

'Ye-es. And he said something — well, it made me think he's hell-bent on getting to me first. I think there's some sort of rivalry going on between those two, Annie, and I seem to be stuck in the middle of it.'

Annie's eyes gleamed. 'Interesting. Do you think Luke's attracted to you?'

Alex snorted. 'Highly unlikely. It's much more likely that it's you he's interested in, especially after this afternoon.' Even she could hear the disgruntled tone to her words.

'Oh-ho-ho, the green-eyed monster's back.'

'I'm not jealous, Annie. For heaven's sake, you know how I feel about him. Annie? Are you listening?'

She wasn't. Instead, her gaze was riveted to the entrance to the pub. Alex turned to look and felt her breath leave her body in a whoosh. Luke was walking in, accompanied by another man. He noticed them in the same instant as she saw him and, without as much as a second's pause, walked over to them.

'Hi, you two. How nice to see you again, Annie.' His smile was a warm one. Alex once again felt excluded. In the next instant, however, he turned to her. 'And you, Alex. Mind if we join you?'

Alex was speechless. Not Annie, however. She immediately chipped in, 'No, not at all — do we, Alex?' Her eyes were gleaming again. Alex's heart did a somersault. She was suddenly unsure what Annie would do next. There was a faintly mischievous look to her friend.

'Oh, um . . . ' Alex stuttered. Luke Rivers was the last person that she wanted to spend the evening with. Especially as she was being forced to spend all of tomorrow with him. She was furious with herself for having agreed to go. And even more with him for having placed her in a position where she'd felt compelled to say yes.

'She doesn't mind,' Annie retorted, thereby confirming Alex had been right to feel uncertain. Alex glared at her.

'This is Neil Forrester,' Luke was saying, apparently oblivious to the undercurrent of tension between Alex and her friend. 'We're negotiating a contract for Forrester Foods to supply my new hotels.'

'How interesting,' Alex muttered. 'Do you need my advice on that, too?'

If Luke heard her, he didn't respond. His gaze was still riveted upon Annie. Why was he here? The Red Lion was a nice pub but hardly one that Luke Rivers would make a habit of visiting, she would have thought. Could he have heard her and Annie fixing up to meet here? It seemed likely. After all, they hadn't lowered their voices. She stared at him. He suddenly swung his head and returned her look.

'We won't bore you with the details, Alex.' He had heard her muttered question. The wretched man must have the hearing abilities of a hawk, she irritably concluded. 'We'll just have a drink with you and then leave you in peace. I'm sure you and Annie have a lot to discuss.'

'Yes, we do. You know, things like what sort of mascara we should buy, what would be the right colour lipstick . . . ' she airily quipped before giving a deliberately foolish giggle. Only to immediately think, good grief! Whatever had got into her? She sounded like the worst sort of airhead.

'Don't be such a party pooper, Alex,' Annie muttered at her side before, in response to Luke's offer to buy them a drink, saying, 'Mine's a white wine; Alex is on the red.'

'No, really,' Alex protested, 'I've just had a large one.'

But he'd already gone to the bar and didn't hear her. Either that, or he'd decided to ignore her. Her lips tightened. He clearly much preferred Annie's company to hers. He couldn't have made that more obvious.

Within minutes he was back, holding a tray of glasses. Alex couldn't help but the notice the eyes of all the other women there following him as he moved. Grudgingly, she conceded that she couldn't blame them. He was extremely good-looking.

'So, what are you two doing here?' he asked.

'Practising our dance steps,' Alex waspishly riposted. Maybe if she was rude enough he'd decide he didn't want her to accompany him tomorrow. She steadfastly disregarded Annie's warning glare.

Sadly however, Luke seemed unperturbed by her sharp retort. 'You could be eating here. We're going to.' His glance subsequently moved to Annie and he smiled.

The man wasn't natural, was all Alex could think. Here she was, doing her utmost to needle him, and all he could do was make eyes at Annie. Alex seemed to arouse no emotions at all in him. Which only intensified her exasperation.

'We're just here for a good gossip,' Annie hurriedly put in, in a fairly futile effort to ease the rising tension round the table. The other man, Neil Forrester, hadn't as yet said a word. Probably frightened to, Alex thought with ironic humour. 'We don't see as much of each other as we'd like,' Annie went on.

Luke smiled at her again. 'You're always welcome to come to the house and see Alex while she's there. You never know, I might be there too.' He lifted his glass in a salute to her.

Annie beamed. 'Hey, I might just do that.'

Alex felt like screaming, 'She's

spoken for, you . . . you lecher.' She didn't, of course. Instead, she took another hefty swig of her wine. Big mistake. Her head swam. She'd had nothing to eat before coming out, she recalled. 'Look, I'm going to have to go.' She stumbled to her feet, swaying slightly as she did so.

Neil Forrester put out a hand to steady her. 'Easy does it,' he said.

'Th-thank you.' He had a nice voice — warm, velvety. He also was quite handsome. Alex hadn't really looked at him till then. She smiled encouragingly. 'How come I haven't seen you a-around, N-Neil?' Her words were very slightly slurred. 'M-maybe you could come and see me while Luke sees Annie?' Oh my Lord! What on earth was she saying? She sounded like some sort of slut, propositioning him. 'S-sorry . . . '

But he was grinning broadly. 'That's okay, Alex. I might just do that.'

By this time, Luke too was on his feet. 'Alex, I'll take you home.'

'N-no. I wouldn't dream of bothering you.'

'It's okay, Luke. I'll go with her.' This was from Annie. Alex was beginning to feel exasperated with them all. Couldn't they see she was just tired?

'I'm perfectly capable of getting myself home.' She swayed again, only this time she completely lost her balance and fell back into her chair. 'You stay, Annie. You're obviously having fun with — with Luke.'

She stared defiantly up at Luke, only to encounter a pair of eyes that held a knowing gleam. The fact that he'd accurately interpreted her jealousy of his and Annie's easy interaction — huh! Why didn't she call it what it was? Blatant flirtation — made her heedlessly plough on. 'I'll tell Rob where you are, shall I, Annie? And who with?'

Annie caught her arm in an iron grip. Her tone when she spoke was one of exasperation. 'Come on, we're going.'

'Are you sure you'll be okay?' This was Luke speaking.

'We'll be fine,' Annie told him. 'You stay with your friend. You have business to discuss.'

* ★ ★ ★

Once they were outside, Alex felt repentant enough to mumble, 'Sorry, I've spoilt your evening. But I just couldn't stay there any longer — not with him. It's bad enough that I have to spend the day with him tomorrow, shopping.'

'What? Annie regarded her with wide eyes. 'You're going shopping with him? What the hell for?'

'Furnishings.'

'Furnishings?' For a moment Annie was speechless. 'Well I wouldn't bet on that, not after the way you've been behaving tonight. In fact, I wouldn't even bet on you still having a job tomorrow. Whatever possessed you, Alex?'

'Have I been that bad?' Alex belatedly felt guilty. Maybe she had overdone the sarcasm?

'Huh! Does the Archbishop of Canterbury pray?'

'Oh dear. I wish I hadn't agreed to go now.'

'Why are you going? You can't stand the sight of the man.' Annie stared at her. 'Or can you? Could it be that you're falling for him — and so you hate yourself, and him?'

'Annie! Luke Rivers is the last man I'd fall for. He needs to furnish his house and, apparently, I'm the only one who can advise him. Simple as that.' She snorted. 'Maybe he should have asked you?'

'Alex,' Annie softly said, 'I think you need to examine precisely how you do feel about him.'

'How I feel about him? I know how I feel about him. Anyway, as I've already said, it's you he's interested in, not me. That's quite obvious.'

'Don't be stupid, Alex. It was you his gaze kept returning to. And he looked decidedly put out when you started flirting with Neil Forrester. No, I think Scott's right. Luke Rivers is attracted to you. I'm just the decoy. Trust me. Now, come on. I'll walk you home.'

★ ★ ★

Alex turned up at Grayling Manor the following morning, her head aching as much with the effort of trying to decide how she should treat Luke after her behaviour of the previous evening — which, let's face it, had been totally unmerited — as with the after-effects of the red wine. What had he actually done wrong? Nothing, that's what. He'd been polite, friendly, and bought her and Annie a drink. And she'd been deliberately rude. She groaned to herself. Maybe Annie had been right and he wouldn't want her to go with him now? Maybe she should just go home again.

But astonishingly, instead of tearing her off a strip, he greeted her with the words, 'I thought we'd make Upper

Linford our first port of call. They've some very good art galleries there, as well as antique shops. What do you think?'

'Sounds good to me.'

Amazingly, he must have decided to disregard her behaviour. If he detected the relief in her tone, he made nothing of it. In which case, she'd take her cue from him and carry on as if nothing at all had happened between them. Least said, soonest mended. Wasn't that what they said?

'Upper Linford is one of my favourite places,' she declared. 'I've spent many a happy hour window shopping. It'll make a change to actually buy something. Not that I'll be buying . . . ' Her words petered out lamely. He was grinning at her almost indulgently. Annie's words of the evening before blazed back at her. 'It was you his gaze kept returning to. Scott's right, he's attracted to you.'

Could Annie and Scott be right? Her breathing quickened. What would she do if they were? How could she have a relationship with the man she'd always held responsible for her parents' deaths?

'Right. Get in then.' He was holding open the door of the Range Rover for her. Obediently, she climbed in.

It felt strange to be sitting in a vehicle next to Luke Rivers and, as they got under way, she allowed herself a sideways glance at him. He was staring straight ahead, concentrating on the road, which meant she had plenty of time to study him unobserved, and with more intensity than she had ever done before.

His profile was a perfect one; no signs of an incipient double chin there. His shoulders were broad, his hands slender, the long fingers riding easily upon the steering wheel. Disturbing images of them caressing her sprang into her mind. She glanced away and out of the side window, her confusion at the riot of emotion that simply looking at him had induced flushing her face.

'If you're too warm, I'll adjust the air conditioning,' he said, completely out of the blue.

'Oh, please, if you would.' Better he think she was too hot than realise the true significance of her blushes.

10

They reached the first of the art galleries that Luke wanted to visit in record time. He drove fast but well, his grasp sure and firm upon the steering wheel, his judgement spot-on. Upper Linford was a small town consisting of just one main street. This was lined on either side with picture galleries, antique shops, book shops, and up-market fancy goods shops.

Luke parked the car and then shepherded Alex into the first of the galleries. By the time they left again, he'd purchased several paintings, the cheapest of which had cost him fifteen hundred pounds.

He smiled at her. 'That was a good start. There's another gallery I want to visit. It specialises in Victorian watercolours and antique porcelain.'

When they eventually left the small

town, the back of the Range Rover was half full and Luke was looking well pleased. Not that Alex had been called upon to offer more than the briefest of opinions. Luke Rivers was proving a man who knew exactly what he wanted and went for it. Which led Alex to wonder why he'd asked her along in the first place.

By the end of the day, the Range Rover was packed to the gunnels and Luke appeared satisfied. He'd also paid for several pieces of antique furniture to be delivered the following week before they'd gone on to a high-quality furnishing store in Dorrington, where he'd ordered the remainder of what he needed. All in all, Alex calculated, he'd spent many thousands of pounds, all without batting an eyelid. It made her bill for the decorating look paltry.

'Right,' he said as they climbed back into the car, 'I think we deserve a drink somewhere, and then we'll go and eat. Would the Sorrento suit you?'

The Sorrento was a very exclusive

Italian restaurant not far from Grayling Manor, in the small town of Kingston Prior. So Alex supposed it could be called Luke's local.

'I thought you needed to book weeks ahead to get a table there,' she remarked.

'Oh, they've always got a table for me,' Luke smoothly retaliated.

Alex's eyes widened in surprise. Although why she should be surprised she didn't know. She was sure that there were very few occasions when Luke didn't get what he wanted.

'Oh well, in that case, fine. I've always wanted to go there — never been able to afford it, though,' she added dryly.

When they stopped on the way back for a drink, Alex discovered she was thirsty as well as hungry. They'd only had a sandwich and a coffee at midday.

'Come on then,' Luke said, after she'd downed her lemonade almost in one, 'let's go and eat.'

'Um, I was wondering about the Sorrento,' she began. 'I'm not really dressed appropriately for such a . . . ' She indicated her casual trousers and shirt, and her flat shoes.

But all Luke said after the briefest of glances was, 'You look fine to me. And, let's face it, I'm not dressed to the nines either.'

Alex continued to look doubtful.

'Alex,' Luke went on, slightly wearily, 'stop worrying. Let's go.'

★　★　★

Once they were seated in the restaurant — to Alex's exasperation, just as Luke had predicted, the maitre d' had had no trouble finding them a table — and had selected the dishes they wanted to eat, Alex decided to do a bit of probing. Not least, to try and discover if Scott's — and now Annie's — assertion that Luke was attracted to her was a correct one. Also, she still knew very little about him.

'Tell me something about yourself, Luke.'

'What do you want to know?' He was leaning back in his seat, regarding her from beneath heavy lids, as his fingers toyed with the stem of his glass.

'What you do each day?'

'Well, I'm a workaholic, as you've probably guessed by now.' He shrugged. 'I buy up ailing companies and try to turn them around. There's not much more to tell.'

'There must be,' she protested. 'What about the hotels you've just acquired?'

His glance was an amused one. 'Touting for business, Alex?'

Stung by this totally wrong assumption, she allowed her indignation to show. 'Of course not!'

'Why not?' He was tilting his head to one side now; his lips were curved in a definite grin. 'If you play your cards right, you could get it.'

Alex didn't know what to say to that. Did he mean it? Goodness! Such a lot of work could make her a fortune, especially at the prices she was charging him for the work at Grayling Manor. But how would she explain it to Ricky and Lauren? She decided to change the subject.

'Do you have any family? Apart from Scott — ' Her words faded. Why had she mentioned Scott? Now he'd probably berate her again.

But apart from a slight hardening around the eyes, Luke disregarded her remark and went on to say, 'Yes. My parents retired to Spain five years ago now. I don't see enough of them.'

'So-o, how come you're not married?'

'Never met the right woman.' A teasing smile flirted with his lips as he said that. Which must be why he'd been reluctant to ask the current girlfriend to help select his furnishings, in case it gave her the misguided notion that she would be the one living in the house with him.

'But you must be what, thirty-six or — seven?'

'Thirty-seven actually,' he told her, his mouth twitching with amusement.

'Thirty-seven,' she exclaimed. 'Rich, good-looking,' she archly said, at the same time provocatively slanting a glance at him. 'How have you managed to remain unmarried this long?'

'I could ask you the same, Alex.' His look was equally provocative as it roved all over her.

Her heart raced. They were flirting. This was just how she'd wanted him to be with her. Daringly, she decided to go with the flow, see where it led her.

'I'm hardly rich, and as for good-looking . . . ' She shrugged. She was blatantly fishing for a compliment. But she couldn't rid herself of the memory of what Scott had said. Or rather implied. Luke found her attractive.

He smiled, his head tilting to one side. 'Oh, you're good-looking all right, Alex. Beautiful, even. But then you know that, don't you?'

'No.' Her heart was beating so hard beneath his lingering gaze that she fully expected it to leap from her chest. She could feel the warmth of a blush colouring her cheek.

'Such modesty,' he murmured. 'Unusual these days.' He continued to appraise her from beneath lowered lids. His gaze was a piercingly intense one. A thrill edged along Alex's spine. She had a sneaking suspicion that she was busy playing with fire. She'd have to take care she didn't burn her fingers — or worse. 'Now,' he drawled, 'let's see . . . You must be what, thirty or thereabouts? Am I right?'

Glad of an excuse to leave such dangerous territory behind, she feigned outrage. 'Excuse me. I'm twenty-nine, actually.'

'So, how come you haven't been snapped up? Are the guys around here blind or something?'

'I'd like to think so,' Alex laughingly admitted. 'But the truth is, as unexciting as it sounds, I haven't had time to get married, or even to go out on a regular basis with someone.' Her laughter faded away as she came rudely back down to earth. 'I've had to bring up Ri-Richard and that's been a full-time job. Not that I've minded.

'Is there no one else who can help? Aunts, uncles, grandparents, maybe?'

'Well, I do have a cousin, L — ' The name froze upon her lips. 'Wh-who lived with us for a while.'

He stared at her for a moment before asking, 'Well can't he or she help?'

'She, and not really. Sh-she's living somewhere else now and really hasn't got the time.'

He sensed she was being evasive with him; she could see that. His gaze narrowed. 'Is there something wrong between the two of you? Have you quarrelled?'

'Oh no.' Not yet, she could have said. Because if Lauren ever found out who she was working for, the fur would fly for sure. But why was he so interested? Because he'd suspected she was keeping something from him? Yet why would he expect her to share private family details with him? It wasn't as if they had any kind of intimate relationship.

'So what is it, then?'

'Nothing. She's got her own life to lead.'

'And so have you. How long did she stay with you?'

'From the age of three.'

'Till when?'

'Oh, nineteen or so — or was it twenty?' Again, she was deliberately vague.

'A long time then. She must have felt like a genuine member of the family.'

'Oh yes, she did.'

'So why would she mind being asked to share the responsibility for Richard?'

This conversation was taking on all the aspects of an inquisition, Alex decided. Although, to give him his due, he did seem genuinely concerned about her. 'She wouldn't. I've just never asked. She's engaged to be married. She just can't give everything up to move back here.'

'Where is she, then?'

'Dorrington.'

'It's hardly the other side of the world. Can't she commute?'

'Richard and I manage fine on our own.' She couldn't tell him that part of the reason — well, a large part, actually — she hadn't asked Lauren to help out was because Ricky blamed Lauren as well as Luke for their parents' deaths. If she hadn't been foolish enough to threaten to take an overdose, their parents wouldn't have had to fly to her side. Oh, Lauren and Ricky still spoke on the phone, but the closeness they'd once shared when Lauren had lived with them was no longer there.

'Anyway, shall we change the subject?' Alex asked.

Mercifully, at that point, the waiter brought their food and after that, the conversation progressed on more general lines. Alex discovered, to her surprise, that she and Luke had lots in common: their love of Vivaldi, as she had already discovered when inspecting his CD collection; their enjoyment of a good book, especially crime thrillers; a penchant for Italian food. The rest of the evening passed effortlessly, and suddenly it was nearly eleven o'clock.

'I'll have to go,' Alex said.

'Richard?' Luke asked.

'Yes.' She decided to come clean. 'Actually, I call him Ricky.'

'Ricky?'

She watched nervously as a small frown tugged at his brow. Would he recall Lauren mentioning the name? Had he recalled it? Was he even now making the connection?

'Seems a shame. I've always liked the name Richard. Mind you, Ricky's a very popular name nowadays.'

Alex allowed herself a small sigh of relief. She'd got away with it. Although why she was so worried, she didn't know. The world wouldn't end if he realised who her cousin was. The chances were, he didn't know that his actions had led to her parents' deaths. To him, Lauren would simply be an old flame. For all he knew, Alex had never heard of him. 'He'll be wondering where I am, and I don't like to leave him too long on his own,' she said.

She prayed she wouldn't find Ricky drunk again. It was happening more and more often these days. He was missing his parents, Alex knew, and she was proving a poor substitute.

She and Luke didn't speak much on the way back to the manor, and once they were there and standing in front of the house, Alex said, 'Thank you for the meal.'

Luke brushed her thanks aside. 'It was the least I could do. You've been an enormous help today.'

Which she knew she hadn't been. She still couldn't understand why he'd asked her along. He'd known exactly what he wanted and had gone straight for it.

'Well, thanks anyway. Um, I thought I might work tomorrow, if that's okay. I'll try not to get in your way.'

Actually, it would be better if she kept completely out of his way; in fact, never saw him again. But that notion induced such a surge of despair that she instantly dismissed it.

'Actually, I'm going to be away for a couple of days — business in Amsterdam. I've got an early start tomorrow, in order to be ready for Monday, so you'll have the house to yourself. It won't be a problem, will it?' His glance now was a keen one. It was as if he were trying to gauge her reaction to his being away. Could he possibly be hoping she'd miss him? The truth was, she would, but she could hardly tell him that.

'No; no problem at all.'

'I see.' There was a distinct edge to his voice. 'Goodnight then, Alex.'

Had she displeased him with her feigned indifference? If so, then maybe Annie and Scott were right? The notion dispatched a thrill of excitement right through her. So much so, that she was oblivious to how close to her he was standing. Which was why the last thing she was expecting was for him to lower his head and drop a kiss upon her cheek. True, it was a brotherly gesture, the same as last time, and once again one that she had no legitimate reason to object to. Nonetheless, Alex was aware of a sharp stab of disappointment; a disappointment that instantly transformed itself into a deep longing to feel his arms around her and his lips upon hers.

It was enough to make her take a step backwards, and not knowing what else to do, she stammered, 'Well, g-goodnight,' before she turned, to practically throw herself into her van.

This was becoming a habit! She turned the ignition key, hoping he wouldn't notice the trembling of her fingers, only to hear the engine groan a couple of times and then die.

'Oh no,' Alex muttered to herself.

She turned the key again. The engine fired. She sucked in her breath. Thank heavens. The last thing she wanted was to be stuck here with the man who, against all the odds and her notion of what was right, she was becoming increasingly attracted to.

11

So disturbed was Alex by that admission that she drove home at a furious pace, at one point only narrowly missing a bollard in the centre of the road. This couldn't be happening; it just couldn't be. She couldn't possibly be falling for Luke Rivers.

She parked the van on the roadside in front of the small terraced house as she always did, there being no driveway, and turned off the engine. The hall light came on inside the house. Ricky was in — and sober, she hoped.

She went inside to find him waiting for her. He looked at her accusingly.

'What's wrong?' she asked, her heart sinking.

'I know who you're working for. Luke Rivers,' he spat.

'Who told you?' Alex quietly asked. She'd never dreamt that Ricky would find out. Too late now to wish she'd been above-board about it.

'Nigel.'

'Nigel? Does he know Luke?'

'Oh,' Ricky sneered at her, 'so it's Luke, is it? How cosy.'

'Ricky, please try to understand. He's paying me a lot of money. How else do you think I could afford your skiing trip?'

'I'd rather not go if he's paying for it.' His voice was beginning to rise; his eyes were blazing.

'He's not paying for it. I am.' She strove for self-control. Rowing wouldn't help, not judging by the mood Ricky was now in. 'How did Nigel know, anyway?'

'His mum knows someone who knows Rivers. Well, she cleans the friend's house, actually.'

'Sorry.' Alex was confused. 'Who cleans whose house?'

'Nigel's mum cleans some woman's house. The woman knows Rivers. She mentioned your name and the name of your business, and Nigel's mum asked him if it was you. Nigel then told me and said who it is you're working for. Nigel's mum is thinking of applying for the job of housekeeper at the manor. She asked Nigel to ask me to ask you what he's like. Apparently Rivers is looking for someone — oh, what on earth does all that matter?' he went on impatiently. 'What matters is that you're working for him.'

'I didn't know he was trying to find a housekeeper,' Alex murmured, still trying to defuse the situation.

'Well, why should you?' Ricky snorted contemptuously. 'You're only his decorator.' He paused, watching her closely. 'You are only his decorator, aren't you, Alex?'

'Of course.' Her response was that little bit too swift, too defensive.

'Yet he took you shopping.'

'He didn't take me shopping. I went along in a purely advisory capacity. I told you.'

'So you did.' He was still watching

her. 'So why is it that I don't believe you? And what, I'd like to know, have you been advising him on till this hour?' He pointedly looked at the hall clock before deliberately turning his back on her and walking up the stairs.

'Ricky, don't walk away from me like that. Let's discuss this.'

He whirled. 'How can you work for — and socialise under whatever pretext — with the man who killed our parents?'

'He didn't kill our parents,' she quietly put in. 'The lorry driver did that.' When had that change of viewpoint happened? Since she'd realised she was falling for Luke?

'Don't split hairs. He as good as killed them. But for him ditching Lauren so suddenly . . . ' Ricky's voice broke and he dashed a hand across his eyes.

'Oh, Ricky darling.' Alex went up the stairs towards him. 'We have to put that awful time behind us.'

He backed away from her; his arm

thrust out to ward her off. 'Don't come near me, Alex. I don't want you touching me, ever again.'

'Ricky,' she pleaded, 'you don't mean that.'

'Yes, I do. You . . . you Judas!'

At that point, her mobile phone rang in her handbag in the hall. Alex swung, torn between going to answer it and staying there, to try and make her brother understand her reasons for working for Luke. The insistent tones of the phone won. She ran down the stairs and pulled it from her bag.

'Yes,' she snapped, 'what is it?'

'Alex?'

'Oh, um, Luke,' she stammered.

She turned to look up at her brother, wondering how he would take the fact that it was Luke Rivers on the other end of the line, only to see — with heartfelt relief, it had to be said — that he'd gone. She heard his bedroom door slam and felt the sting of tears fill her eyes and lodge uncomfortably in her throat.

'Are you all right, Alex?' Luke was asking.

'Yes — um, no — uh, yes.' But it was hopeless. She couldn't stem the flow of tears. She felt so alone. She'd have given anything, absolutely anything in that second, to have her parents back again. 'I'm fine. S-sorry, I-I c-can't talk now.' She switched off before Luke could hear her deep-throated sobs.

She went into the kitchen and there gave free rein to her misery, telling herself over and over that she should never have taken the job at Grayling Manor. She'd known that, yet still she'd gone ahead and done it.

The doorbell rang, startling her. It was a prolonged angry sound, as if someone had placed their finger on it and held it there. She dried her eyes and went into the hall. Who on earth could it be at this hour? The last thing she felt like was receiving visitors.

She glanced into the mirror on the wall. Her eyes were swollen and red, the lashes spiky with the tears that were still clinging to them; it was perfectly evident that she'd been crying. She patted them dry with her handkerchief and then opened the front door.

Luke stood there.

Horror, stark and all-encompassing, shook her. Supposing Ricky heard him? What then? It would all come out, every bit of it. Ricky had never been one to hold back. She whispered, 'Luke!' and then glanced fearfully up the stairs. Thankfully, there was no sign of her brother. Yet he couldn't have helped hearing the doorbell, surely?

Rather than invite Luke in and risk Ricky overhearing, she stepped outside and pulled the door to behind her. Her brother slept in the back bedroom, so with any luck he wouldn't hear anything.

Luke was regarding her with a strange expression now. 'I only rang to make sure you'd got home okay, as the van had sounded iffy again, but you sounded so upset. I was concerned, and

I looked up your address in the phone book.'

He sounded almost . . . defensive. Alex had never told him where she lived. A deliberate omission on her part, but then again, he'd never asked.

'Sounded upset? Did I?' Alex tried to laugh the notion off. The trouble was, it came out as a strangled sob. Instinctively, she bowed her head, hoping to hide her face from Luke's penetrating scrutiny.

She should have known better. For he, too, simply bowed his head, the better to look at her, as he placed both hands upon her shoulders. 'Yes. Alex — you did. What's happened?'

His kindness — tenderness, almost — got the better of her desire to appear untroubled by anything more serious than tiredness. She found she couldn't speak, so she simply shook her head. She didn't know why she was so distressed. After all, it wasn't the first row she and Ricky had had, not by any means.

But this one had been different. He'd never looked at her in quite that way before, with unmistakable contempt, no matter how heated their row had been. Her tears started again, and she couldn't halt them. It was as if something inside her had finally broken free. She hadn't really wept, not like this, in the aftermath of her parents' deaths. She'd had Ricky to think of then, and she'd tried to control her grief for his sake as much as anything else. But now she sobbed with heart-wrenching abandon, letting all her grief, so long suppressed, flow out of her. Not caring that it was Luke Rivers who was witness to her complete and utter breakdown.

Luke pulled her in to him, wrapping both of his arms about her. 'Alex,' he murmured, 'sweetheart. What is it? Tell me.'

'I c-can't,' she wailed. And then, in direct contradiction of what she'd just said, 'It's Ricky.'

'Your brother? What's he done?'

'N-nothing,' she sobbed, which was a patently ridiculous thing to say. If Ricky had indeed done nothing, why was she crying her heart out?

Luke didn't speak. He simply held her while she cried herself out and the tears slowly dried. She sniffed unbecomingly, dragging her hand across her nose. What must she look like? She prayed her nose wasn't running. A snowy white handkerchief was waved in front of her.

'Oh, thanks,' she gulped. 'I have got one somewhere — '

'Use that one,' Luke said.

Alex blew her nose and then wiped her eyes. 'Sorry. I'll wash it and return it. Sorry.'

'Don't apologise, Alex. Something's really upset you. Would you like to tell me about it?'

'I can't. It's between Ricky and me. He misses our parents — ' She dashed a hand across her face. ' — as I do.'

'Come on. Let's go inside and I'll make you a cup of tea.'

Alex couldn't seem to find the words to say no. Instead she let him lead her in, and silently she pointed to the door that led into the kitchen. Luke quickly filled the kettle; located the teapot, the tea, the cups and saucers; got the milk from the fridge and found the sugar bowl in another cupboard. He moved efficiently, silently.

Alex watched in bemusement, totally beguiled by the sight of this man — rich, successful, surely more accustomed to being waited upon rather than waiting on — performing this most mundane household task. Alex couldn't help herself: she grinned.

Unfortunately, Luke chose that moment to swing and face her.

'What's so funny?' An answering grin spread across his face.

'Nothing,' Alex murmured. She belatedly remembered something then. He'd called her 'sweetheart'. Sweetheart. She'd heard it quite clearly. And, in spite of her sadness, her heart began to sing.

'Didn't think I was this domesticated, huh?'

'Something like that.' Happiness bubbled out of her, making her want to jump for joy. She watched, entranced, as he poured boiling water into the teapot, then stirred it briskly with a spoon before pouring milk into two cups and adding the tea to it. 'Sugar?' He quirked an eyebrow at her.

'No, thanks.'

'Here you are, then.' He grinned at her again as he handed her a cup.

They sipped their tea in companionable silence and then Luke set his cup and saucer down, saying, 'If you're okay, I'd better get off. Things to do ready for my trip tomorrow. Not least, unpack the car.'

Alex's heart dipped a little. She'd quite forgotten he was going away. 'I'm fine.' She'd seen yet another side of him tonight. He was certainly a man of many facets. Which one was the true one? she mused. 'Thank you,' she added, 'for coming round.'

'My pleasure, Alex.' He was staring at her, his expression a quizzical one.

Alex wondered what was coming now. Yet another surprise? Knowing Luke as she was coming to, it wouldn't be out of the question.

She waited.

A moment or two passed. Alex finished her tea and set the cup and saucer down. That seemed to be the signal that Luke had been waiting for.

Because he strode over to her and once again took her by the shoulders. There was no sign of uncertainty, not by as much as a heartbeat. He pulled her close, just as he'd done outside. This time Alex didn't bow her head. She stared straight back at him. So she saw the exact second that the glints appeared in the dark eye and his head swooped to hers.

12

Luke's lips brushed hers tantalisingly; heart-stoppingly. What changed that, Alex had no idea. All she did know was that what began as a light, almost comforting caress, rapidly changed into the full-blooded, passionate kiss that she'd been yearning for only a half an hour or so ago.

For a split second Alex struggled, more against her own heated emotions than his boldness. But then the longings which she had been suppressing for days now took over and with a small moan, she gave in to them.

Luke folded her even closer, his arms tightening as his kiss deepened. She heard him groan deep in his throat. Alex had never experienced anything like it before. Her lips involuntarily parted and his tongue plunged within, creating a desire and urgency that she was powerless against. She only knew she wanted him with every fibre of her being — just as he clearly wanted her.

It was that admission that awoke her to the danger of what she was doing. She jerked herself away. Luke Rivers was the last man she should be kissing. What if Ricky had come down? That thought alone was enough to make her widen the distance between them. She and Luke . . . they could never . . .

'Alex? What is it?'

'We shouldn't have done that.'

'Why not?' He looked surprised; taken aback. 'We're both adults. We know what we want.'

'I know, but — please. You and me . . . It isn't possible.'

'I don't understand. You're a free agent, aren't you?' There was once again an edge to his voice, a razor-like quality to his gaze.

It sent a shiver of misgiving through Alex. Luke Rivers was someone you toyed with at your peril, as had already been brought home to her more than once in her dealings with him. She blurted out the only response she could think of: 'No.'

'No?' The single word was like a whiplash. It left Alex feeling exposed, every one of her nerve endings raw and vulnerable. 'You gave me the impression this evening that you were. That there was no one.'

'I-I lied. Sorry.'

She watched as his expression changed. What had started out as disappointment changed instantaneously into dark fury. His fists clenched at his sides. Alex flinched. He was going to hit her.

'So who is he?'

'You wouldn't know him. He-he's working abroad at the moment.'

He hadn't taken his eyes off her since she'd first said she wasn't a free agent. It was as if he were trying to see into every part of her, read her every thought. He spoke in a low voice. 'And does he know you go around kissing other men in his absence?'

'I don't go round kissing other men.

And just to set the record straight, you kissed me.'

He gave a snort. 'I didn't notice you complaining. In fact,' he added, looking her up and down now, his expression one of barely concealed contempt, 'as I interpreted it, you couldn't get enough of it,' he finished crudely. 'I know when I'm kissing a willing woman and boy, were you willing.'

'I'm sorry. I didn't know.'

'Oh please, don't give me that old chestnut. You didn't know what you were doing? You knew exactly what you were doing. Pressing yourself against me, inviting . . . ' He stopped there. His gaze was a shuttered one now. There was no sign of the familiar glints. 'I didn't have you down as a tease, Alex.'

'I'm not a tease,' she spluttered.

'Really? Well, what would you describe yourself as then?'

Alex was too stricken to speak. He was right, of course. The anguish of that admission was like a knife going into her. She'd been playing with something she hadn't understood. She didn't know what Luke would be capable of. And now, he despised her — and rightly so. She had led him on, whoever had started the kiss. Because she was sure that if she'd made any sort of protest, he'd have halted things right there and then. And now, she'd compounded her fatal mistake by saying she wasn't free. It was too late to undo it. If she tried, he'd have every excuse to brand her a liar as well as a tease.

'Oh, don't look like that,' he snapped. 'I'm going. Good job I'll be away for a couple of days, isn't it? Give us both time to . . . cool down.' He looked her up and down again; it was a withering, yet at the same time provocative, glance and Alex practically cringed beneath it. 'Goodnight, Alex. I'll see myself out. Oh — ' He swung back to her. ' — just get the job finished as quickly as you can, please.'

He didn't actually put it into words, but Alex had no doubt what he meant:

'So that I never have to set eyes upon you, ever again.'

★   ★   ★

When Alex let herself into Grayling Manor the following morning, she found herself praying that Luke wouldn't still be there. She didn't think she could face him. She'd already had another set-to with Ricky and that was enough for one morning. Still, she sighed, at least her brother hadn't ignored her, so she supposed that was something to be grateful for.

Mercifully, the house was empty, but that didn't stop her starting work with a heavy heart. The image of Luke's contempt had stayed with her all night. He hated her, despised her — and who could blame him? She'd brought it all upon herself. The second his lips touched hers she should have pulled away. She knew any relationship between them was doomed before it started. Whatever had she been thinking of?

She was working in the drawing room when Ricky came calling. He was the last person she'd expected to see, given his hatred of Luke.

'Thought I'd see the place where the infamous Luke Rivers lives for myself. Is the great man at home?' He was practically sneering as he took a look around.

'No, he's away for a couple of days. How did you get here?' Grayling Manor was a bit too far from their house to walk.

'Bus. It stops virtually at the end of the drive.'

'Oh, I see.'

'So come on, show me around.'

Alex was surprised at this unexpected interest in Luke and his house. She wouldn't have thought Ricky would want to be within a hundred miles of the place. She silently led the way out of the room. Alex didn't have the heart to remonstrate with him about coming here — not when they seemed to be on the verge of becoming friends again. So although it felt wrong, she showed him the completed dining room before leading him into the 'snug' and then Luke's office.

'It's not fair,' Ricky suddenly burst out, pointing at the television, the DVD, the expensive laptop. 'He all but murders our mum and dad and ends up with all this.'

'Ricky, that's not true. They died in a road accident. Nobody murdered them.'

'Well, he might as well have done. It was his fault — his and Lauren's,' he muttered.

Alex could see it was no good trying to argue with him, not while he was in this sort of mood. But she could try and put Luke's case. The incongruity of that, in the light of her own past feelings about what had happened, once again struck her forcibly. Yet she knew she had to try and make Ricky see Luke in a fairer way. As she now did. 'He's worked hard for what he's got.'

'Huh! He disgusts me. He doesn't deserve any of this.' He swung a leg and kicked the base of the door, chipping the paintwork in the process.

Alex immediately and rapidly ushered him out of the room. She shouldn't have allowed him inside. This was Luke's home, his place of sanctuary, and no matter what he'd done — or not done — he deserved to have his privacy respected.

Back in the hallway, Ricky flicked a glance around at the antique furniture and the paintings, then scathingly said, 'I'm surprised he hasn't got the place full of little winking lights and alarms.'

'He will have soon, I'm sure.' Maybe he should have had an alarm system fitted? After all, he'd bought some valuable items yesterday. Where were they? she wondered.

She regarded her brother. Something in his remark and the glance he'd given made Alex uneasy. 'Ricky? Why did you come?'

'To see where he lives. Know your

170

enemy, isn't that what they say?'

'He's not our enemy. It's all in the past. We can't change anything.'

'Wanna make a bet?' Ricky cynically asked.

Alex found it hard to settle back into her work after Ricky had gone. But settle she had to. Luke had been quite specific. He wanted her finished and out of his house.

As if the past twenty-four hours hadn't been bad enough, that evening Lauren phoned. She and Alex hadn't spoken in weeks, a fact that Alex had intended rectifying but just hadn't got round to.

'Lauren,' Alex exclaimed. 'It is good to hear from you.'

'What's going on, Sandra? I hear you're working for Luke Rivers. How could you?' she burst out.

'Ricky,' Alex muttered in exasperation. 'He told you.'

'Of course he told me. He rang me. He's really upset, and so am I. Do — does Luke know who you are?

That-that you're my cousin?' She sounded nervous; fearful, even.

Alex frowned. Why would Lauren be nervous? Or fearful? Angry, yes. 'No. I haven't said anything.'

'How could you, Sandra?' Lauren burst out. No signs of nervousness now. She must have imagined it, Alex decided. 'After the way he treated me.'

'I'm sorry, Lauren, but I needed the money. Beggars can't be choosers and unlike you, I don't have a live-in lover to help with the bills. And isn't it time you called me by my proper name? Alex?'

'To me, you'll always be Sandra — and there's no need to be sarcastic. It's not my fault you aren't in a relationship. Maybe if you weren't so fussy.'

'Fussy?' Alex cried. 'The chance, and the time, would be a fine thing. I have a business to run and a younger brother to look after. I haven't noticed you offering to help out.'

'I would if I could. But you know how it is.'

'No, I don't, Lauren. Why don't you tell me how it is?'

'Well — ' Lauren was on the defensive now. ' — I do have a job and a demanding private life.'

But Alex was already feeling bad about the way she'd spoken to her cousin. 'It's all right, Lauren. You don't have to explain. I do understand, really. But please, don't ring me up and tell me how to run my life. When you're prepared to help out — '

'Oh, there's no talking to you, is there?' And with that, Lauren slammed the phone down.

Alex stared at the receiver in her hand through a haze of tears. Now she'd upset Lauren too. That must be a record: three people in twenty-four hours, more or less. Maybe she should just give up the job at the manor? That should please everyone. But she knew she wouldn't do that. She'd never, ever walked out on something halfway through and she wasn't about to start now. No, she'd double her efforts and finish in record time. That should satisfy everyone — except her, that was.

For all of a sudden, and despite knowing it was the only way forward, the prospect of never seeing Luke again was an impossibly bleak one.

13

Alex decided after that to start work early and finish late. It was the only way to end all of this: by finishing the job and leaving Grayling Manor, and Luke Rivers, behind her.

The next morning she was ready to go by seven. She went into the hall to pick up her keys, amongst which she'd clipped the one that Luke had given her. That way, she'd reasoned, she wouldn't lose it.

They'd slid partly behind the phone. She prised them out. She must have knocked them when she'd been talking to Lauren.

Quietly, she let herself out of the house. She'd left a note in the kitchen for her brother. She had called up the stairs to him but there'd been no answer. Normally, he'd be up by now too; for some reason, he must be tired.

He'd been out the evening before, but she'd heard him come in and it hadn't been late. She hoped he wasn't hung over. He had to go to school.

The road to Grayling Manor was deserted. Only one other vehicle passed her, which meant she made the journey in record time. She was parking the van in her usual spot when she noticed that the front door to the house was ajar.

Her heart sank. Luke must be home. From what he'd said, she'd assumed he wouldn't be back until this evening at the earliest — if then. She walked inside, bracing herself for confrontation. All the doors leading off the hall were standing open. She frowned. That wasn't like Luke. He always kept them closed. She poked her head into the 'snug' and it was then that the truth hit her.

Luke wasn't home. The house had been burgled.

There were just gaping spaces where his television and his DVD and CD players had been. Alex ran into Luke's office and found the same thing there: everything was gone. Only his desk and chair were left.

She took the stairs then, two at a time, frantic to check the bedrooms. Where had he stored all the things they'd bought? They must be up here somewhere. If they'd gone as well . . .

She flung open the first door she came to and breathed a deep sigh of relief. They were all there. He must have decided to wait until the decorating was finished before placing them around the house. She went back downstairs and called the police, after which, somewhat reluctantly, it had to be said, she rang Luke on his mobile phone.

'Right.' His tone was brusque and cold in the wake of what she'd told him — he clearly hadn't forgiven her for what he saw as her lies. 'I'll be back in a couple of hours with luck. I'm sure I'll get a flight with very little problem. The one out was half empty.'

As Alex replaced the receiver of the

phone, a police car turned up. The interview didn't take long; after all, she couldn't tell them very much. She knew what was visibly missing, but if Luke had kept money or jewellery anywhere she wouldn't know.

One thing the police were able to tell her was that there were no signs of a break-in. 'The thieves must have had a key. Do you have your own key, Miss Harvey?' one of them pointedly asked.

Alex nodded.

'Who else besides yourself and Mr Rivers has one?'

Alex was uncomfortably aware of the suspicion in their gazes. She swallowed nervously and said, 'Um, Mr Rivers's brother, Scott; but other than that I'm afraid I couldn't say.'

'Okay,' the older of the two policemen said. 'We'll need to go and see this Scott. Do you have his address?'

Alex said, 'No.' She hadn't seen anything of Scott since Luke had come upon them kissing. His invitation to go out had never materialised. She wondered now whether Luke had had a hand in that.

'When are you expecting Mr Rivers back?'

Alex told them.

'We'll come back then.' And that was that; they left.

★   ★   ★

Despite his optimism, it was the middle of the afternoon before Luke strode in. He barely looked at Alex, and when he did his face was set and implacable. 'So what's missing?' he demanded to know.

'Um, things from the snug and your office: the televisions, DVD and CD players, your laptop. That's all I know about. All the doors were standing open; that's how I knew . . . ' Her voice trailed off. He didn't ask her how she knew what had been in those rooms in the first place, so he must have guessed she'd had a look previously. However, he didn't comment on that. 'The police are coming back to see you.' She followed him into his office. 'Um, they wanted to know who had a key. Apparently there's no sign of a break-in.'

He swung to face her at that. For a moment, he didn't speak. 'I take it you've still got yours?'

Alex's heart missed several beats. Was he accusing her? 'Yes.'

'And you haven't let it out of your possession?'

'Of course not. I always leave it on the hall table at home, but other than that . . . ' Her voice faded away. Her keys hadn't been in their usual place. She'd assumed she'd knocked them. Oh no — not Ricky. Surely he couldn't have . . . wouldn't have? She racked her brains to try and recall whether she'd seen them during the evening, because that was when Ricky had been out. But she couldn't remember. She was so used to seeing them in the same place that she didn't really notice them anymore. But what if he'd simply removed the key to Grayling Manor from her key ring and left the others on the hall table? She certainly wouldn't have noticed then.

'Yes, Alex? What?' He was studying her intently.

'Nothing. I've always been very careful with it.'

She could see he didn't believe her. She felt the incriminating flush creeping up her face. 'If you don't trust me — '

He didn't answer that. 'Don't let me keep you from your work,' was all he said before he strode away from her in the direction of the stairs.

Feeling wretched beyond belief, Alex watched him go. She'd been well and truly dismissed.

★   ★   ★

That evening when Alex arrived home, Ricky was waiting for her. He was on edge — frightened. Alex felt sick. She had to know, though. She began to speak, her voice jagged and raw.

'Grayling Manor was broken into last night. Please tell me you didn't take my key, and — '

The fear gave way to defiance. Ricky's face flushed red. 'Yes, I did take your key. I gave it to Nigel.'

'But I heard you come in. You weren't late, and I'm sure I'd have noticed if my keys weren't on the table when I went to bed.' But, as she'd reasoned before, would she have?

'I came home as usual, waited a couple of hours till you'd gone to sleep, and then I went out again. I took the key from your key ring then.'

'Oh no,' she moaned. 'Oh, Ricky, how could you? Did you actually help him to steal the things?'

'No, I just stood lookout outside.'

'But that makes you an accomplice!' she cried. 'How could you be so stupid? What am I going to tell Luke?'

'Nothing, if you've got any sense. Nigel doesn't like people talking about him. Anyway, why are you worried? Mr High-and-Mighty can easily afford to replace everything, even if it wasn't insured, which I'm sure it was.'

'That's not the point. You've committed a criminal act.'

'Not really. Nigel did all the thieving. He carried the stuff out, him and a mate, and they'll dispose of it. I didn't actually touch any of it.'

⋆　⋆　⋆

Alex tossed and turned all night, struggling to decide what she should do. In the end, as dawn broke, she got up, and after several cups of tea set off for Grayling Manor.

Luke was nowhere to be seen, not surprisingly. It was still only seven o'clock. Eventually she heard him moving about, but he didn't come into the drawing room. Which was just as well, because she still hadn't decided what to do about Ricky. How could she shop her own brother? How could she not?

Luke did eventually come in to see

her. 'Aah, good,' he said, looking around. 'It's coming on.' He was still distant, granite-faced. So he hadn't forgiven her for what he considered her provocative teasing, and probably never would if Scott were to be believed. How could she possibly tell this man that her brother had stolen her key and given it to a friend?

She couldn't, of course. She didn't know why she'd ever thought she could. Ricky already felt betrayed by the fact that she was working for Luke. How could she betray him a second time? Because, rightly or wrongly, that was how he'd see it.

'Have you heard anything from the police?' she nervously asked him. 'About the burglary?' She dreaded glimpsing the first signs of accusation within his eye.

'No, nothing. They've dusted for fingerprints but there's so many all over the place that that's not much help. I doubt they'll find who's responsible. Only Scott, you and I have keys, so — '

He shrugged. ' — someone must have been careless.'

He meant her, of course. Did he suspect her? If he did, he didn't say so.

'Well, I-I've been very careful,' she haltingly said.

'I'm sure you have.' His tone was dismissive; curt. She sensed he was about to wipe her from his life, just as he'd done with Lauren. Her heart ached as she admitted, finally and too late, that she'd fallen deeply and unconditionally in love with him.

'I'll maybe see you later,' he said. 'Goodbye.'

★   ★   ★

The following day, she was progressing with more speed than she had anticipated on the drawing room walls when she heard the front door open. Surely it couldn't be Luke back already? What was he doing, checking up on her in case she was about to steal anything else?

185

14

But it wasn't Luke. It was Scott.

'Scott!' Alex exclaimed. 'Luke's not here.'

'I haven't come to see Luke. I've come to see you.'

'Oh?' He wasn't going to make another pass at her, was he? Her heart sank. Looking at him now, standing there, looking so much younger than Luke, so ... immature, she couldn't imagine why she'd ever thought she could have begun any sort of relationship with him.

'To warn you.'

'Warn me! What of?' He was starting to make her feel nervous.

'Luke thinks it's you.'

Alex stared at him. 'Thinks what's me?'

'The robbery. He thinks you did it.'

'What?' Alex's stomach heaved as she

absorbed the implications of what he was saying.

'You're the only one with a key other than him and me, of course. He thinks you got some help.'

'I'd have needed it to get all those things out. Who does he think I enlisted to assist me in this . . . this burglary then?' She was desperately trying to stay cool, not to sound in any way guilty. Not that she was guilty of anything other than allowing her brother into the house, and what a mistake that had been.

Scott shrugged. 'Haven't a clue. He didn't share those suspicions with me. Of course, I don't think it was you, not for a single second. Alex — ' He moved towards her.

Alex took a step back. 'He actually said that? That he thinks it was me?' Surely if Luke thought that, he would have accused her to her face? Whatever she'd thought of Luke Rivers, she'd never had him down as a coward.

'Yes.' He couldn't quite meet her eyes

— too embarrassed, obviously, by what he'd had to tell her.

'Scott? Are you sure of that?'

He glanced up at her, his expression defiant. 'Yes. You may not want to believe it, but it's true.'

'I see.'

'What will you do?' He was watching her intently.

Good question, thought Alex grimly. What was she going to do? She couldn't tell Luke the truth; she'd already decided that. Ricky would never forgive her. It would be the end of the family, as small as it was.

'Thank you for telling me, Scott. Now if you'll excuse me, I have work to do.'

'B-but surely you're not going on working for him? Not now. Not after what I've just told you.'

Once Scott had gone — angry with her for not immediately walking away from the house, Alex suspected — she stood, unmoving, her mind a maelstrom of anguish and indignation. So

Luke thought the robbery was her doing. No wonder he'd been so cold. And no wonder he hadn't answered when she'd implied he didn't trust her. Yet she still found it puzzling that he hadn't confronted her with his suspicions. She'd practically invited him to accuse her.

Unless . . . A shiver of dread passed right through her. Perhaps, instead of accusing her, he was intending to go to the police.

She covered her face with her hands. They were shaking. She could end up in court over this, possibly even prison. But common sense raised its head at that point. Neither Luke nor the police could prove anything against her. Okay, her fingerprints were plastered all over the place, but then they would be. They certainly couldn't pin this on her. Nonetheless, Scott was right; she couldn't go on working here, not now. Not only did Luke deem her a tease, but he now thought her a thief as well.

With hands that refused to stop

shaking, she tore a piece of paper from the notepad that she used to jot down details for her quotations, and removing Luke's key from her key ring, she placed it to one side of this. Her note was simple and to the point. She told him that she knew he believed she was the thief. She didn't mention Scott's name. She didn't want to get the younger man into any sort of trouble. He had been good enough to warn her, after all. 'You probably won't believe me, but I had nothing to do with the break-in. So, under the circumstances,' she wrote, 'I'm sure you will appreciate that I can't continue working for you. I'll send a bill for the outstanding amount of money due, less the work which I've left unfinished. I'm sure you'd prefer to find someone else to complete it for you. Alex.'

★ ★ ★

She was busy preparing dinner and trying, without a great deal of success, to put the events of the past couple of days from her mind when she had a visitor.

It was Scott — again.

'I hope you don't mind, but . . . well, I saw the note you left for Luke and although I implied that you ought to stop working for him, I still feel as if it's my fault you've left. I'm sorry.'

It struck Alex, however, that he didn't look sorry.

'No, Scott. I appreciated you telling me the truth,' she said. 'I know how hard it must have been.' So, why did she feel that he wasn't being totally honest with her?

'I just want to say again that I don't believe for a second that the burglary was down to you. Luke is right out of order.'

'Thank you, Scott. It's nice to know someone trusts me. Um, do you want to come in?' She spoke reluctantly. His look of . . . triumph, almost, dispatched a ripple of unease through her. There was something he wasn't telling her.

'I'm in the middle of getting dinner, actually.'

'Thanks, I will.'

She nibbled at her bottom lip. She'd been sure he'd refuse her invitation. It had only been made out of courtesy. 'Cup of tea, or something stronger?'

'A glass of wine would be nice.'

Why, oh why had she asked him in? Goodness knew how long he'd stay now. What if Ricky turned up? Would he be as hostile to Scott as he was to Luke? 'Red or white?'

'Oh, red, I think.'

She was in the process of uncorking the bottle when she heard the sound of the front door opening.

'Sandra, it's me.' It was Lauren. Of all times for her cousin to show up.

'In the kitchen, Lauren.'

Behind her, Scott gave a gasp. 'Lauren! What — ?' Then, 'Sandra? You're Sandra? She talked about you all the time.' He was looking at her in astonishment.

Before she had time to ponder the

strangeness of all of this, Lauren breezed into the kitchen. 'After our phone call, I thought we needed to talk — Oh, my God! What's he doing here?'

Alex looked from one to the other of them. They looked . . . guilty. Why should they look guilty?

Thoroughly confused by this, Alex asked, 'Lauren, what is it? Obviously you know Scott. I assume you met him while you were seeing Luke?'

She glanced again at Scott. He was staring at her cousin as if he couldn't believe his eyes. 'How-how — ?' he stuttered.

Lauren ignored him and mumbled, 'It's a long story.' Both of them were beginning to look as if they wanted nothing more than to run from the house.

'We've got plenty of time.' Alex spoke slowly. She, too, was staring intently at Lauren. 'By the way, Scott, this is my cousin, Lauren Baxter. She called me Sandra because she always has — couldn't master Alexandra as a little girl. Sandra stuck, I'm afraid.'

Lauren glanced from her and back to Scott again. 'You're going to hate me, Sandra!' she wailed.

'It's Alex, Lauren; Alex. And why will I hate you?'

'I didn't quite tell you the truth about what happened between me and Luke.'

'What?'

'I was unfaithful to him with Scott.'

'What!' Good grief, was that all she could say?

'He found us together; that's why he broke it off with me.'

Alex shook her head, as if by doing that she'd be able to put her chaotic thoughts into some semblance of order.

'I felt so ashamed. I was only trying to make him jealous; to make him care for me properly. He was only ever . . . well, fond of me, I suppose. I wanted more. I wanted him to love me.'

'You were trying to make him jealous!' Scott blurted, as if that were all that mattered.

'Yes. And it all went horribly wrong. Instead of caring more for me, he finished things — which meant that Scott was no longer interested in me either, were you, Scott? If Luke didn't want me anymore, then you didn't either.'

Scott hung his head. For once, he had nothing to say.

'Is that why you told Mum you were going to kill yourself?' Alex furiously demanded. 'Because you felt ashamed?' She almost spat the final word. She didn't see Scott's look of horror as she practically shouted those words.

'I didn't really intend to do anything; it was a silly threat.' Lauren spread her hands, her mouth twisting into a shaky grimace. 'You know me, Sandra — sorry, Alex. Ever the drama queen.'

Alex couldn't help herself. She flew at her. She began to shake her. 'They rushed to you, and were-were both killed for their trouble.' The tears began, flowing in a torrent down her face. 'How could you, Lauren? How could you?'

Scott strode to Alex and put an arm about her.

Past caring who she offended now, or who she hurt, Alex turned on him too. 'Get your beastly hands off me! I see it all now!' she raged. 'You're so envious of Luke and what he's achieved, you have to steal what you think he wants. First Lauren, now you try it on with me. How many others have there been, Scott?' Scott's continuing silence was an admission of guilt to Alex. 'Well, this time you've got it all wrong. He doesn't want me.'

'Sandra — ' Lauren began.

'It's Alex, Lauren — Alex!' she shouted, almost beside herself with rage and grief.

'Alex, don't you think I've blamed myself every second since they died? That's why I hardly come near you or Ricky any more. It was all my fault.' Her voice broke.

'But why didn't you tell me the truth afterwards? Why let me go on blaming Luke?' Alex demanded.

'I was frightened to tell you,' Lauren moaned, 'when I'd been the cause of the whole thing. You'd have hated me,' she sobbed. 'I'm so sorry, Alex. I never dreamt you and Luke would meet.'

The doorbell rang again. Alex felt only relief. Anything to stem this relentless flow of anguish. She went to open it, oblivious to the fact that her face was still streaming with tears.

Only to find herself staring at Luke.

'Alex.' He took one look at her and stepped inside, quietly closing the door behind him. He then took her into his arms. 'I'm so sorry that I should have made you think that I believed you responsible for the burglary. I have never thought that, not for a single second. Please, don't cry.'

'It's not that,' she continued to sob. It felt so right to be in Luke's arms. 'Not you,' she gulped. 'It's — '

'What? What is it? Tell me.'

Alex pointed towards the kitchen. 'I'm so sorry. I've blamed you all this time.'

Luke was frowning now. 'Blamed me? What for?'

'Come in.' She pulled away and taking his hand, led him into the kitchen.

Scott looked in horror at his brother.

'What on earth are you doing here, Scott?' Luke demanded to know. His keen glance took in the one other person standing there. His brow lowered into a frown. 'Lauren?' He glanced back at Alex. 'What's going on?'

Both Scott and Lauren began to speak at once. Lauren said, 'Alex is my cousin. I only ever called her Sandra, which is why you haven't realised — '

While Scott said, 'I came to see Alex because — '

'Yes, Scott,' Luke quietly put in, 'because what? Because you were intending to make another pass at her?'

It was Lauren who answered that question. 'I don't think you need to worry about that any longer, Luke.' She paused, looking if anything even more stricken than she'd looked moments ago. 'I think there's something you should know.' And she went on to tell Luke the truth of what happened after he had finished with her. She held nothing back; she told him all of it. About how she'd said he'd dumped her, out of the blue, for no reason. About her falsely threatened suicide, and their parents' fatal car crash as they rushed to be with her.

As she finished speaking, Luke turned to Alex. 'And you blamed me for all of this?'

'Yes. I'm sorry. I should have realised once I knew you that you wouldn't be that callous.'

'Well, I can be a bit of an ogre at times, or so people tell me.' He looked at Scott then.

Scott was much subdued. 'I had no idea that Lauren had threatened to kill herself, or that she was using me.'

'As you were using her, eh, Scott?' Luke sounded bitter. 'To get at me. It strikes me now that you were very well suited.'

'Yeah, well, sorry. It won't ever happen again. You have my word.'

'It had better not, or I won't be answerable for the consequences.'

★   ★   ★

Once Scott and Lauren had left, both distinctly shamefaced, Alex turned to Luke. She had no intention of telling him that it was Scott who'd falsely said he was blaming her for the robbery, doubtless to scupper any possible chance of her and Luke getting together. She didn't want to make things even worse than they already were between the brothers. But there was one thing she had to confess to. 'Luke, it was Ricky. He took your key from my key ring and gave it to some other boys. They carried out the burglary. I'm sorry. If I hadn't left your key on the hall table — '

Luke silenced her with a look. 'Tell him that if they return the stuff, or as much of it as they can, I'll take the matter no further. It's all replaceable.'

'Really?' Alex gasped.

'Yes. You've clearly both been labouring under a misapprehension about me, so . . . ' A glimmer of a smile was now tilting the corners of his mouth. 'It explains a lot actually. The barrier I'd always sensed there between us, for a start.'

Alex didn't know what to say to that.

'There is no one else, is there?' he went on to ask. 'No one working abroad? That was just your excuse for ending a kiss that you felt was wrong.'

'Yes.' Alex couldn't look at him in the aftermath of that admission.

'Look at me, Alex.'

She did as she was told.

'So in that case, can I take it as read that you feel the same way as I do?'

'We-ell, it depends on how you feel.'

He reached out for her and yanked her towards him, straight into his arms. 'I would have thought you'd have known that by now. I tried hard enough to show you,' he muttered.

'Maybe you'd better show me again, just so that I can be sure?' She looked up at him through a fan of eyelashes. 'Tease that I am.'

'You can tease all you want,' he murmured throatily, 'as long as I get my way with you in the end.'

'Oh well, in that case . . . ' Alex murmured, parting her lips seductively.

'Witch,' Luke murmured right before he bent his head and claimed her lips in a kiss that took her breath away; a kiss that went on and on and on . . .

'Don't you know I'm crazy about you?' he finally said once they surfaced for air.

'I think I'm beginning to suspect that.'

'So in that case, when do you think you'll be able to finish the decorating?' he demanded with a teasing smile.

'Oh!' She retaliated by playfully slapping his arm.

He immediately put on an air of wounded innocence. 'I mean the whole house, naturally. You can have a free hand, providing you will think about living in it with me.' His eyes darkened until they were nearly black. 'I've fallen in love with you, Alex, and I'd like to think we'll spend the rest of our lives together.'

'Would Ricky be able to come along? I mean, after all that's happened? I couldn't leave him.'

'My darling, your whole damned family can come along if it means I have you with me.'

'But are you sure? I mean, we haven't known each other very long.' Although it felt as if she'd known him always. Her soul mate.

'It's been long enough for me.' His expression softened to one of heart-aching tenderness. 'I knew you were the one the first time I set eyes on you. Nothing that has happened since has changed that. I want to court you, love you.' His voice grew husky with passion. 'Make you feel the way I do.'

'Oh Luke.' She smiled at him. For all his outward self-confidence, something in his gaze told her that he wasn't as sure of his ability to do all this as he sounded. 'I already do.'

'Good.' The dark eyes blazed with happiness — and love. 'So let's get down to the really important business, shall we?' And he pulled her back into his arms.

THE END

THE CAPTAIN'S WIFE

Jean Robinson

1975. After years struggling to cope with a childless marriage and the loneliness of being left behind while her seafaring husband Max is away, Sarah finally persuades him to take her with him on a four-month voyage. But she is not prepared for the change in him once in command of his ship, and often feels resentful that he has so little time for her. Over the months she and Geoffrey, the chief officer, are drawn together for comfort, and perhaps more — but is that what Sarah really wants?

THE BREAKING WAVE

Sheila Spencer-Smith

Harriet owes a debt to Rick Seton's family, and to repay it she gives up her job to help Rick set up the Breaking Waves Surf School in Roslarren. But there are problems — notably the arrival of Jem Williams, intent on finding a suitable venue for his geology courses, for which their building would be suitable. Attracted to Jem, Harriet strives to remain loyal to Rick's interests. Can the two be reconciled and Harriet and Jem find lasting happiness together?

THE HOUSE OF RODRIGUEZ

Wendy Kremer

When schoolteacher Anna escapes to Spain for a holiday, sparks fly when a misunderstanding on her very first day there leads to confrontation with Isandro, an arrogant architect. Despite their initial falling out, she comes to know his sister Teresa and her children — though Isandro's girlfriend Maria is anything but welcoming. Gradually drawn into the warm, close-knit family, Anna even begins to thaw towards Isandro. But after the fallout of a past relationship, she is wary of ever opening her heart to anyone again . . .

EARTH MAGIC

Linda M. Priestley

Physically and mentally scarred after a terrible accident, Claire is bullied by a gang of youths one day while walking through the park — and then Jake steps in to help. Working with him in his garden, Claire finds peace and a purpose in life, along with the first steps towards friendship and, perhaps, even love. But the harsh practicalities of their lives threaten to terminate the enchanted hours they spend together on the allotment, and Claire begins to wonder if she and Jake can ever have a future together . . .